BUGS TO BLIZZARDS
OR
AN ARMY WIFE AT
FORT D. A. RUSSELL

BY
MARTHA FLEISHMAN
AND
CAROL JOY JUSTICE

Published by

Wigwam Publishing Company
Cheyenne, Wyoming

Printed by

Pioneer Printing & Stationery Co.
Cheyenne, Wyoming

First Printing, May 1974
Second Printing, December 1974

Cover photo courtesy of Wyoming State Archives

PREFACE

This book is designed to present historical information about Fort David Allen Russell, Wyoming. The characters Alice, Charles, Richard, and son William are ficticious. All other characters are real persons who were stationed at or involved with Fort D. A. Russell. Historically valid situations are contrived for the characters, with the intention of presenting an accurate picture of life at the Fort.

It would be impractical to give appropriate thanks to all of those who helped us. There were too many to number. Special thanks are in order, however, to the staff of the Wyoming State Library and the Wyoming State Archives and Historical Departments.

All of the artwork in the book was done by wives of military men stationed at F. E. Warren A. F. B., formerly Fort D. A. Russell. Their cooperative effort has added greatly to the fun of this project.

Working on this book has provided the authors with insight into the military reservation where they now live as well as hours of mutual enjoyment together. We hope we are able to share some of this enjoyment with you.

Martha and Carol

DEDICATION

To our own military men—Marty and Jack

Fort D. A. Russell, W. T.
February, 1868

Dear Alice,

We arrived in this forsaken land of prairie. I must admit I was not prepared for Fort D. A. Russell although I had seen its beginnings in early fall. At that time the Post consisted of tents only. Not realizing we would be stationed here—the tent Post made little impression upon me.

"Now frame quarters for a regiment have sprung up into a small village but the surroundings are destitute of any green to relieve the eye. Wind constantly sweeps the parade ground bare and drives the garrison almost to despair with its monotony." I long for the quiet of some sheltered eastern Post.

We have just moved into our Officer's quarters. We share our double house with two lieutenants. We have five rooms, three downstairs and two bedrooms on the second floor. The rooms are so drafty and primitive as the inside has planed boards and battens instead of plaster. The two bedrooms, each with a big closet, have a door connecting and others opening out on the narrow landing above the stairs. Each has a sharply sloping roof and dormer window. The front room looks out on the parade ground. The view from the rear windows is lonely and desolate. I am told that even in the summer the yard, like all its fellows, is bare and brown for nothing will grow on such soil.

The great relief from the monotony of life here, is our Sundays. The Post Chaplain E. B. Tuttle and his wife ride with us to the school house in Cheyenne for worship. The three mile trek provides ample time for light conversation. The school house is newly completed and approximately seventy-five souls respond heartily to Rev. Cook's sermons.

I am sure by the tone of my letter, you can tell how anxious I am for your company, and am looking forward to your arrival this summer.

Your Loving Aunt,
Elizabeth

Merril J. Mattes, *Indians, Infants, and Infantry* (Denver: The Old West Publishing Co., 1960), pp. 175-176

Medical History of the Post, Microfilm H-62, Wyoming State Archives

Capt. Charles King, *Marion's Faith* (J. B. Lippincott Co., 1892), Page 175

Shirley E. Flynn, *Our Heritage* (Pioneer Printing Co., Cheyenne, Wyoming, 1968), pp. 18-25

Description of Post.

OFFICERS' QUARTERS.

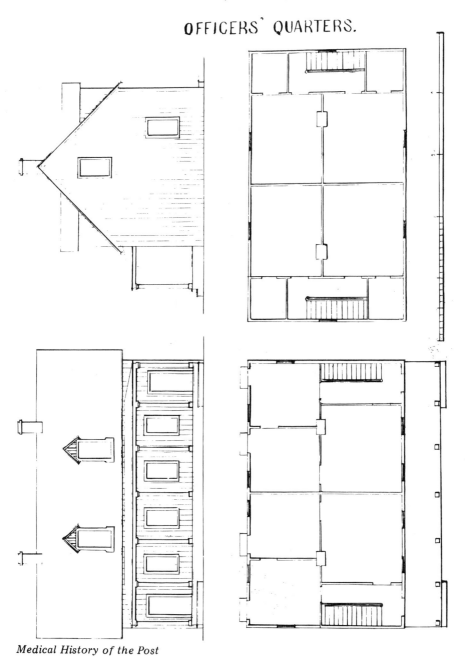

Medical History of the Post

Dear Diary,

I spent the last part of my trip reading the *New Overland Tourist and Pacific Coast Guide* which gives a description of all the towns in which the train stopped. The last morning was spent acquainting myself with the sections on Cheyenne and the Post.

Upon arrival I got directions to the Rollin's House where I met Aunt Elizabeth in the parlor. We took tea in the main dining room before embarking on an ambulance wagon ride to Fort D. A. Russell. Aunt Elizabeth said that she uses the ambulance for all of her visits to town.

As we drove out of town, we passed Ford's Saloon, Glover's Drug Store, the Dodge House, and the Magnolia Laundry on O'Neil Street.

Cheyenne seemed to end abruptly and then we continued on an open, desolate plain for one and one-half miles. We stopped at Cheyenne Depot to pick up two soldiers returning to the Fort. Then we rode one and one-half miles further west to the entrance of the Post.

I was surprised to find there was no stockade around Fort Russell. The Post formed a diamond shape, 800' x 1040', with the Commander's House at the northern apex and the Guard House directly opposite across the parade ground. On the East side of the Commander's house were seven double Cavalry Officers' Quarters. The West side had matching quarters for Infantry Officers. Aunt Elizabeth had described them well to me in her letter. The Southern Portion of the diamond was formed by Cavalry and Infantry barracks.

Arriving mid-afternoon, Uncle Andrew was relaxing on the front porch, talking with Major Burrowes and his wife, before 5:00 recall. The gentlemen carried my trunks to the back second floor bedroom where I will be living.

Being exhausted from my journey, I retired until dinner.

Diaries and Letters of the Reverend Joseph W. Cook, Laramie Republican Company, Laramie, Wyoming, 1919

Indians, Infants, and Infantry, Merrill J. Mattes, Old West Publishing Company, Denver, Colorado, 1960

Medical History of the Post, Microfilm H-62, Wyoming State Archives

Ft. Russell taken from a painting dated September 20, 1868. *Courtesy of Wyoming State Archives.*

Dear Diary,

I have just spent my first full day at Fort D. A. Russell. After a light breakfast, I was introduced to my new surroundings by Aunt Elizabeth.

All the quarters on the west side of the parade ground where I am living, are occupied by Infantry Officers. We walked across the parade ground between the Cavalry Officers' quarters to the Post Hospital. Aunt Elizabeth introduced me to Dr. Charles Alden, the Post Surgeon. My Aunt had arranged for Dr. Alden to show me the Post in his ambulance. I stepped on the mounting box and boarded the front seat. We headed south, past Dr. Alden's house and the Post Trader's House, to the Post Trader's Store. Here we stopped and I met the proprietors, Mr. Wooley and Mr. Hugus.

The Store was a low wooden building standing just north of the entrance gate of the Fort. Inside, the middle room of the store was fitted up with a couple of old-fashioned billiard tables, a huge coal stove, some rough benches, chairs, two or three round tables, and the inevitable bar and cigar stand. It bore on the portals the legend "Officers" as distinguished from the "General Club Room" beyond. Mr. Wooley explained that the men spend most of their time hunting, playing billiards, or drinking.

We continued our ride passing the front gate and the road to Cheyenne which I traveled on yesterday. The Cavalry barracks and kitchens were on one side, as we drove further south toward Crow Creek. The air was filled with fragrances of hot baked bread, as we passed the Bakery. Dr. Alden said they baked enough bread for the total troop strength of 367 men.

Crow Creek came into view. According to Dr. Alden, Crow Creek is a "small and torturous but never failing stream." On either side of the creek are bluffs from thirty to fifty feet high with many small bottoms between them. Along the creek a few low willows and wild currant bushes grow.

Dr. Alden had to return to the Post Hospital, so I decided to finish my sightseeing on foot. As the ambulance headed up the steep hill toward the Guard House, the mules startled several jack-rabbits from their hiding places in the tall grass.

I walked along Crow Creek surrounded by color. "The desolate prairies and bottoms are made brilliant by a profusion of wild flowers,

Capt. Charles King, *Marion's Faith*, J. B. Lippincott Co., 1892, p. 93
Medical History of the Post, Microfilm H-62, Wyoming State Archives
Records of the Office of the Adjutant General, Reservation File, Fort D. A. Russell, Wyoming, Record Group 94, National Archives

rich in number rather than variety." The walk was lovely, but by the time I arrived home, I was tired from the combination of the walk and the altitude.

The afternoon was warm, and the odors from the open sewers drifted up to my room, making sleep difficult.

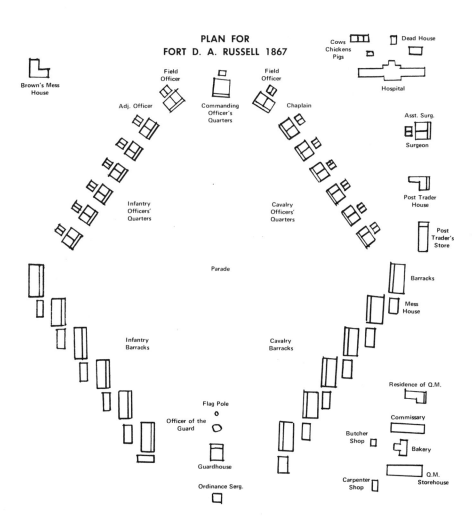

PLAN FOR
FORT D. A. RUSSELL 1867

11

Dear Diary,

Looking back on the summer, it would have been impossible to foresee the chain of events that would change my life.

It all began that day in July, when Dr. Alden was called away and left me on the banks of Crow Creek. His patient was a young wife of a Second Lieutenant who had a severe case of dysentary. She had arrived only recently from the East and was unable to adapt to the living conditions here on the Post. Dr. Alden explained to us after her death that dysentary rapidly weakened her and she contracted the fatal affliction-pneumonia.

Aunt Elizabeth and I crossed the parade and joined several others who had come to pay their respects to the widower Charles. I found him to be a handsome and pleasant gentleman. After a week of solitary bereavement, Charles came to call. On the frontier it is difficult to survive alone.

It seems strange that today I am preparing for my wedding with this gallant officer.

Aunt Elizabeth has fitted her wedding gown to me beautifully. The gown is of white silk taffeta. The bodice is trimmed with silk fringes and ruched white net; the sleeves of ruched silk and the cuffs of plain silk. The back fastening skirt, with a deep box pleat, is accented by tiny bows that extend to the floor. A white silk apron with rows of ruching and a deep border of gathered net, completes the gown. The veil is of very fine applique bobbin lace on machine made spotted net.

It is well that I am shorter than Aunt Elizabeth, as the gown trails the floor. No one will notice that my shoes are inappropriate.

I am so pleased that Aunt Elizabeth offered the gown to me and that Uncle Andrew will stand up with me.

The living room has been "beautifully draped with the greatest number of flags of all sizes—each one a regulation." The fireplace is thickly covered with ropes and sprays of fragrant western pine boughs and wild flowers.

Most of Charles' regiment are lined up outside to greet us after the ceremony. They all look so handsome in their full dress uniforms. The Captain of my future husband's company shall be the best man. Charles also has no family in the west.

Frank R. Keefer, *A Textbook of Military Hygiene and Sanitation*, W. B. Saunders Co., Philadelphia, 1917, p. 73

Nancy Bradfield, *Costume in Detail: Women's Dress 1730-1930*, Plays Inc., Boston, 1968, pp. 223-226

Frances M. A. Roe, *Army Letters from An Officer's Wife 1871-1888*, D. Appleton and Co., New York, 1909, pp. 348-349

My stomach is unsure of its future, but my mind is determined. Aunt Elizabeth has proved to me that the riggers of an Army wife are sometimes trying, but always exciting.

I shall start my new life in Charles' quarters, across the way from Aunt Elizabeth, bringing with me the lovely gifts from officers and friends alike. "A case containing sixty handsome small pieces of silver was given by the Officers of the Post." A superb silver pitcher was given by Dr. Alden and the two hospital stewards. Many of the ladies of the Fort have given me handsome linens to grace my new home. The refinement of the East has been offset by the friendliness of the West.

Mrs. Tuttle just came to my room to inform me that her husband, the Reverend, is ready to begin.

Gini White

October 1868

Dear Diary,

We are almost settled in our new home. Our quarters consist of three rooms and an attached kitchen in the rear. This forms one-half of a double set of Cavalry Officer's quarters.

Charles "has placed his furnishings (some lace curtains, camp chairs, and a carpet) in the living room, and there is a forelorn-looking bedstead in the bedroom. A pine table in the dining room and a range in the kitchen complete the outfit. A soldier has scrubbed the rough floors with a straw broom. It is absolutely dreary, and my heart sank within me when I first saw it."

Aunt Elizabeth told me that I would have to learn to be a "plucky" Army wife. However discouraging my surroundings, it would be my wifely duty to perform miracles and turn this "brass-buttons" home into a comfortable and attractive abode.

I initially turned my attention to the kitchen. The Quartermaster Department furnished everything in the way of kitchen utensils. I was "surprised to find nothing smaller than two gallon tea-kettles, meat-forks a mile long, and mess-kettles deep enough to cook rations for fifty men! I rebelled and said I would not use such gigantic things" but Charles reminded me that when the Regiment moved, a Second Lieutenant was allowed only 1,000 lbs. of baggage. I should try to make do with the issue items provided me. Boiling eggs in huge pots in this altitude may be a continual source of irritation.

The next area which required my immediate attention was the Army of bugs that "came in during the day and marched upon us at night." They seemed to seek refuge from the chilling fall winds through the cracks. These houses are built of rough boards placed upright with the cracks battened. The inside is finished with planed boards and battens instead of plaster. Crow Creek mud used as battens, crumbles at the slightest jar from wind or touch. This provides easy access for creeping things of all descriptions. Since I fear their invasion, I work continuously cleaning and filling cracks with a mixture of newspaper, flour, and water.

My wifely duties include taking our laundry to the Laundress' pine slab quarters across Crow Creek. She had been working for my husband previously.

Vanished Arizona, Martha Summerhayes, J. B. Lippincott Co., New York, 1963, pages 12-14

Army Letters from an Officer's Wife, Frances M. A. Roe, D. Appleton and Co., New York, 1909, p. 81 and 58

Wyoming Annals, "History of Ft. Francis E. Warren," Jane R. Kendall, January, 1946, p. 9

The Gentle Tamers, Dee Brown, University of Nebraska Press, Lincoln, 1968, p. 164

I am fortunate that Charles' former wife owned a sewing machine. There are no ready-made womens' clothes and all the women on the Post anxiously await the issue of *Harper's Weekly* sent by Col. Bartlett's sister in the East. *Godey's Lady's Book* also provides us with current fashion styles. Many yards of linsey-woolsey and calico are cut from designs in these magazines.

I am looking forward to my first trip to town as a married woman. The wives at the post are going and I will enjoy shopping for my own household.

Dear Diary,

The ambulance arrived at our quarters at 7:30 A.M. Mrs. Tuttle was already aboard. She was ready for our shopping trip to town with a long list of items that she would need for their trip to St. Louis.

I stepped onto the mounting box and entered the ambulance from the rear. Due to the November winds, the flaps on the ambulance were down. The only view was out the rear where I entered, or looking over the driver and four mules at the front. This ambulance was designed to accommodate eight wounded men, but the liters had been replaced by two long, wooden benches running the length of the wagon, with a narrow aisle in between.

I sat facing Mrs. Tuttle as the ambulance continued around the diamond. We picked up Mrs. Van Vost, and Aunt Elizabeth.

Between the front gate and Camp Carlin we discussed our shopping needs. Mrs. Tuttle was specifically looking for yard goods for a traveling outfit for her journey. Aunt Elizabeth and I were both looking for household items and groceries. Mrs. Van Vost was anxious to check the Post Office for mail order items.

The ambulance stopped a mile and a half from the Fort at Camp Carlin, where Mrs. Carling joined our party along with Joseph, the "black boy" who works for her.

Leaving Carlin, I could see Cheyenne through the front flap of the ambulance. Although it is a mile and a half to the city, there is nothing to block one's view. The plains stretch flat and empty in all directions. No wonder Cheyenne is called "The Magic City of the Plains" for it seems to have sprung from nowhere. Within a year this tent town has turned into a city of 5,000 inhabitants.

Private Larry L. McGunmess stopped the ambulance in front of the Post Office on the 200 block of West 16th. We agreed to meet in two hours. Mrs. Van Vost was disappointed when Mr. Thomas McLeland, the Postmaster, informed her that her items had not arrived.

Our next stop was the Union Mercantile. There were "barrels of crackers and pickles, and cans of kerosene and axel grease. Sugar was measured by a scoop into a paper bag; coffee beans were ground by hand; and a big round cheese was carelessly sliced with little regard given to weight." Aunt Elizabeth paid her monthly bill and was given a bag of candy.

At the meat market I was given soup bones and liver free. Here I

Cheyenne Leader, July 9, 1868. p. 1, col. 3, Wyoming State Archives

Magic City of the Plains, Wyoming Centennial Historical Committee, July 1967, pp. 69 and 100

Vanished Arizona, Martha Summerhayes, J. B. Lippincott Co., New York, 1963, p. 15

purchased a live hen to fulfill our household needs. Aunt Elizabeth examined the available hens carefully and helped me select one. Joseph carried the crate for me. This, along with Mrs. Carling's parcels created a humorous scene. Joseph could hardly see where he was going, and it appeared as if parcels were walking by themselves.

At the tin shop, "I saw the most beautiful array of tin ware shining and neat, placed in rows upon the shelves and hanging from hooks on the wall." I couldn't resist the temptation and bought a stock of tin-ware and had it charged to Charles' account. "I feared that the tinware was to be our bone of contention," so I decided not to mention it to him. A month will be soon enough! Perhaps the holiday season will temper his anger.

As we made our way back to the Post Office, the streets were thawing under the warm November sun, and the mud made it difficult to navigate.

On the return trip to the Fort, the pleasantries of the day lessened, as the tin-ware loomed heavily on my mind.

16th Street, Cheyenne, 1868, *Courtesy of Union Pacific Railroad Museum Collection.*

Dear Diary,

Time has gone faster than I anticipated since Charles left in late April. Scouting trips to Fort Fetterman and Fort Laramie, summer maneuvers, and Major Van Vost's five company march to Atlanta, turned Fort D. A. Russell into a female compound.

As soon as spring set in, Indian Bands began pilfering in the surrounding countryside. In June, the 5th Cavalry gave chase to a band of Cheyenne on the Republican River who attempted to stampede a mule herd. Thank goodness the hostiles never encroach upon the fort.

The summer social activities continued even though there was an obvious lack of men. We did have enough for the first baseball game played by the "Wyomings of this city and the Franklins, of Fort Russell." The game resulted in a signal victory for the Franklins by a total of thirty-nine runs to twenty. The *Leader* suggests that "the disparity of the play between the two clubs is probably due to the fact that the Wyomings have just organized and had no practice, while the Franklin Club is an older organization and in good play."

In early May there was a large celebration and demonstration to welcome the new territorial officers. "Our spirits were dampened by a sudden rain but we gathered in McDaniel's Hall and listened to a few words from Governor Campbell, General Lee, Secretary of Wyoming, and Judge Hower, Chief Justice." I was much pleased with the appearance of them all. They look like pleasant gentlemen.

We also celebrated the completion of the Union Pacific Railroad. The May 10th *Leader* states that at 12:49 Cheyenne time the final stake was driven into the railroad tie. With the phrase, "Tie Done" the transcontinental railroad was completed.

We also attended the Theatre Comique. Three plays were presented; "Perfection," "Sublime and Ridiculous ' and "Betsy Barker." Mr. William Chandler, the actor, displayed talent of a versatile character and was received with great favor by the patrons of the theatre.

Much of the summer was spent canning fresh fruits and vegetables. My tinware proved helpful.

Since Aunt Elizabeth and Uncle Andrew are now at Fort Laramie, I decided to visit them during Charles' absence. I was permitted to travel with the Paymaster in the Army Dougherty. I found this wagon

Returns from U.S. Military Posts—Ft. D. A. Russell, Microfilm No. 617 Roll 1050, National Archives, June 1869

Cheyenne Leader, May 10, 1869, p. 2, col. 3

Diary and Letters of Reverend Joseph W. Cook, Laramie Republican Co., Laramie, Wyo., 1919, p. 124

Cheyenne Leader, May 10, 1869, p. 2, Wyoming State Archives

to be more comfortable than the Army ambulance used for short trips. I spent two weeks keeping Aunt Elizabeth company and returned refreshed and full of new ideas for our quarters.

I expect Charles' company back within the month. I have repapered the bedroom and again filled the cracks with newspaper, flour, and water, hoping to hold out the ravages of winter for one more year.

December 1869

Dear Aunt Elizabeth,

Cheyenne has been a hot bed of political activity. The Territorial Legislature has passed some astounding acts. One in particular I can't wait to tell you about. It is an act granting every woman of age twenty-one years, and residing in the Territory, the right to VOTE!

Charles assumes that this act will be repealed within the year. He is treating the whole matter as a foolish mistake, as are many other men. The *Cheyenne Leader* seems to agree. The following appeared in the newspaper on December 11th:

> "Governor Campbell yesterday approved the Female Suffrage Bill, thus making it a law of the Territory. We now expect at once quite an immigration of ladies to Wyoming. We say to them all, come on. There is room for a great many here yet. When Wyoming gets tired of such additions to her population, we'll agree to let the outside world know of the fact. Won't the irrepressible "Anna D." come out here and make her home? We'll even give her more than the right to vote—she can run for Congress!"

This bill was passed on the last day of the session of the Legislature. It was stated in the newspaper that the men were very tired after a long and fruitful session.

Major Burrow's wife heard from Asst. Surgeon Henry Parry, a most interesting tale of how this came about. It seems that in early September of this year, a woman named Esther Morris had a gathering at her home in South Pass City. She is a strong proponent of women's suffrage. She had invited two Territorial Representatives in an effort to enlist their support of the female suffrage bill.

I don't know if the story of her persuasiveness is true, but the bill was approved December 10th, to the chagrin of many males.

I suppose most women will not concern themselves with involvement in matters of this sort. I am not sure how I feel, but if Charles' reaction is any indication, then women will not gain from such a measure. It certainly has made interesting talk among the women here at Fort D. A. Russell.

I must close my letter, but I have one surprise to share with you. Although I have not told Charles because he is out on escort again, I think his return last fall will be remembered by an eventful spring!

Love,
Alice

Cheyenne Leader, December 11, 1869, p. 1, col. 1, Wyoming State Archives
Medical History of the Post, Microfilm H-62, Wyoming State Archives

Big Wyoming **Pamphlet**

February 1870

Dear Diary,

After the small pox scare of the summer, the men and children were vaccinated by regiment. The threat of the disease moved from downtown Cheyenne to the Post. Even Laramie city had reportable cases. At Fort D. A. Russell the men and children were vaccinated at the Post hospital by Asst. Surgeon Charles Mackin. I felt sorry for those whose shots did not take.

I have just returned from having my "pinch" at the needle. My whole body feels feverish and sore. Mackin explained that thus far today, fourteen had been revaccinated successfully, and sixty had been revaccinated unsuccessfully. Modern science may be a blessing—but I shall feel more secure once I know the shot does not have to be repeated.

Although I feel hot, today is crisp and cold. Charles tells me that the Quartermaster Department is now issuing buffalo overcoats and buffalo overshoes to all soldiers who are exposed to severe weather. That means most soldiers at this Post will have one before spring. I understand from Mrs. Wentworth, a laundress whose husband stands sentry duty, that the coats have a distinct odor. I wonder if my present condition will permit its presence in our home?

My dear friend, Mrs. Van Vost, left in December with her husband for a new assignment. Mrs. Van Vost was behind most social events here at the Post. She will be greatly missed. Everyone is hopeful that the social functions will continue, helping to ease the monotony. Lt. Col. Thomas Duncan has now assumed command of the Post.

It is possible "our home" will shortly include another family. Housing seems so scarce and Officers and families continue to arrive. We have been lucky thus far to remain in the same quarters. The tradition of bumping in the Army, leaves one fearful for his home and bed.

Record of the Medical History of the Post, Film H-62, Wyoming State Archives, pp. 109 and 117

Letters Received Quartermaster Department, No. 191 and 193, Record Group 393, National Archives

General Orders No. 36, December 1868, Fort D. A. Russell, Wyo., "Authorized Laundresses", Group 393, National Archives

Returns from U. S. Military Posts—Fort D. A. Russell, Microfilm No. 617 Roll 1050, National Archives

Artifacts courtesy of Wyoming State Museum

April 1870

Dear Diary,

There has been a lot of activity at Fort D. A. Russell in the last months.

Rows of cottonwood and spruce were planted around the Officers' quarters and the hospital. They look somewhat spindly in the wind but perhaps in a few years they will provide shade and a break from the monotonous prairie.

During the month most of the Officers' quarters were lined with tarred sheating paper. We are hopeful ours will be done also.

Gravel walks and roads are starting to be laid. It certainly should improve my daily walking in inclement weather.

I have arranged for Mrs. Smith, a laundress and wife of a soldier, to help me during my confinement. She will continue her regular work as a laundress but will stay with me at night for the first week or so. She has no children of her own but has helped other women during their time.

I have been feeling tired and find my strength somewhat limited. With Charles away on patrol so often, keeping the fires going and cleaning up the dust and black coals, takes most of my energy.

My clothes are uncomfortable and I shall be relieved when summer brings baby's arrival. The clothes I wear have made the rounds of many western posts. I should not complain as I have not had to concern myself with a wardrobe for this period.

Much of my time has been spent making a warm baby quilt. It has a bright calico top with turkey track stitch separating the blocks. Several layers of flannel add to its warmth. The back layer is of a dark denim given to me by Mrs. Smith.

Some of the other Officers' wives have been working on sacques for our baby. We are not the only family from the Post who will add to the 1870 Territorial census this summer.

Medical History of the Post, Microfilm H-62, Wyoming State Archives, May 1870, pp. 165 and 169

An Army Doctors Wife on the Frontier, University of Pittsburgh Press, 1962, p. 50

25

Dear Diary,

Some of the ladies of Fort D. A. Russell gave me a "confinement party." I am convinced their motives were good but they frightened me with tales of western childbirth practices.

They told me about American Indians who hastened the labor of their women by placing them on the prairie and having a horseman with hatchet raised, ride straight at them apparently intending to trample them. The fear inspired resulted in a short labor.

Another effective means was to insert snuff in a woman's nose. It made her sneeze incessantly which brought on labor quickly.

Ancient methods of inducing labor were discussed such as tying a woman's hands and feet to a stake and having two men lift the stake and drop it abruptly to the ground numerous times.

They all laughed as these tales were described, but the teasing tormented me. Mrs. Alden assured me this is not done in this day and age. Thank goodness our son, William, was cooperative for after five days of confinement he was born with Dr. Alden's assistance.

William is now three weeks old and my strength is returning nicely.

This morning at 10:00 Charles sent a note saying our set of quarters had been selected by a cavalry officer who had just arrived at the Post. We had to be out by 1:00. Charles was involved with the Officer of the Guard and it would be impossible for him to help move our things out. "At first I was dazzled and wholly incapable of comprehending the situation—it seemed so preposterous to expect anyone to move everything out of a house in three hours." "The manner in which it was done was humiliating in the extreme." I sat and looked forelornly at the trunk that was to hold all of my worldly possessions.

At that moment Charles walked in and introduced me to Capt. Chambers. He realized the situation and graciously suggested we share the quarters with he and his wife.

We have not been driven out of our house—but have given the second level to the Chambers. We will share the kitchen.

Will I ever get used to being an Army wife?

Devils, Drugs, and Doctors, By Howard Haggard M.D., 1929, Blue Ribbon Books, Inc., New York City, p. 68

Doctors of the American Frontier, By Richard Dunlap, Doubleday, 1962

Army Letters from an Officer's Wife, Frances M. A. Roe, D. Appleton and Co., New York, 1909, p. 66

Dear Diary,

I have found living with another family very difficult. Mrs. Chambers prefers preparing meals privately so we use the kitchen in shifts. I wonder now if it was wise to remain on the first floor since they traffic our two rooms regularly. Privacy is a luxury of the past.

This has not been my only problem of the last month. There has been a great scarcity of vegetables and no fish at Fort D. A. Russell. Even before the Companies left on summer maneuvers, some had been without potatoes for three months. The Subsistence store on the Post lost many items from imporper storage. Officers' flour, condensed milk, as well as lima and green beans, had to be destroyed. Dr. Corson has done everything in his power to bring fresh fruit and vegetables up from Denver.

To complicate matters, the doctor has said that too much refuse matter has been allowed to accumulate in the rear of the Officers' quarters. There is no systematic way of emptying and carrying away the slops. Officers' families here keep chickens and some even have cows. "Usually this is to the irritation of neighbors and the indignation of the Post Surgeon, who is charged with maintaining standards of sanitation." "The sinks and other open holes around the Post are a constant problem and have become filled with putrefying refuse . . ." which could become the source for an epidemic among the troops.

Flies abound. The flies are so numerous that they even manage to get through the gauze to the baby. Charles has been amusing himself catching flies. For the past half hour he has been killing them and putting them in the wash basin. He has over eighty now.

The whole situation is upsetting but the demands of the day leave me no time to fret.

Letters of the Subsistence Officer, p. 65, 9 May 1870, Record Group 393, National Archives

Medical History of the Post, Microfilm H-62, Wyoming State Archives, Dec. 1870, p. 199

Frontier Regulars, by Robert M. Utley, Macmillan Pub., 1973, p. 89

"The Role of the Army Surgeon in the West" By David Clary, *Western Historical Quarterly,* Jan. 1972, Vol. III, No. 1, p. 59

An Army Doctor's Wife on the Frontier, University of Pittsburgh Press, 1962, p. 29

D. Douglass...

November 1870

Dear Diary,

Orders arrived yesterday. Charles is to proceed to Fort Fetterman by month's end. I will be so pleased to leave this boarding house and have a home of my own again. We really don't know what awaits us but the change will be a relief.

Charles has promised me a trip to Denver and we leave on tomorrow's train. Since our new Post is far from any city, we will purchase one bolt of bright material to take care of our sewing needs for the next few years.

My Fort D. A. Russell curtains may accommodate us in our new home. If not, I will use them for clothing for baby William and myself. Mrs. Chambers will now have the responsibility for the whole house. She has already questioned me about any items I might want to sell or leave behind. I told her my beautiful tinware would go with us.

Charles brought in two large Army chests. Along with my own trunk, all of our belongings must go into them. He told me we were allowed 1,000 lbs. of baggage when he changed station.

"I was pitifully ignorant of the details of moving, and I stood despairingly gazing into the depths of these boxes." A neighbor came in and offered her assistance. I carried everything into the living room while she knelt on a pillow and meticulously packed the chests.

"I found we had a great deal of surplus items which had to be put into rough cases, or rolled into packages and covered with burlap."

Charles "fumed when he saw it, and declared we could not take it all, as it exceeded our allowance of weight. I decided we must take it or we could not exist."

Concessions were made by both of us, and the job of packing was done!

Vanished Arizona, Martha Summerhayes, J. B. Lippincott Co., New York, 1963, pp. 7-20

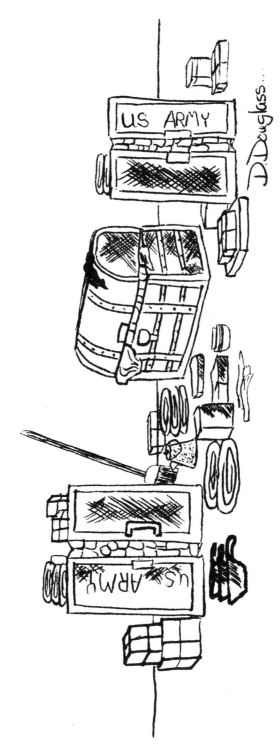

Dear Diary,

What an exciting trip we had to Denver!

The Army ambulance took us to the station where we boarded the four car train for the five hour trip. The seats were most comfortable but I was most upset with the appalling practices of the travelers who shared our car. I couldn't seem to make myself at ease with my surroundings. All the windows were closed to keep the lightly falling snow and wind out. The air inside was filled with cigar smoke, people in need of bath, and odors from garbage strewn on the floor.

When my nauseous condition required the opening of a window, the cinders flying back from the smokestack singed my clothing and irritated my eyes. A linen duster had been suggested for the trip, but I did not own one.

Other things added to my aggravation such as the obvious lack of the proper receptacle for the disposal of tobacco juice. I am so thankful baby William sits nicely in our laps.

The token effort made by the Union Pacific brakeman was to sweep with a broom just wide enough to make a path down the center aisle. He did this two times during our trip down. Due to these conditions, Charles and I found it most difficult to enjoy the picnic lunch I packed. We were both relieved when we saw Denver coming into view.

Stepping off the train, the sky was blue and the pure air intoxicated me. The Ford House was opposite the depot and the People's restaurant was nearby on Blake Street. The packed snow made walking easy.

Denver's streets were very wide and lined with trees. Houses were attractive, and numerous public buildings lined the avenues. "Everywhere are stores, banks, hotels, and saloons. One would hardly believe himself at the end of the prairie 2000 miles from New York."

We purchased not only our personal needs, but those of friends at Fort D. A. Russell. Daniels and Eckhart on Larimer Street had an unusually fine selection of cotton goods, dry goods, cloths, and

Doctors of the American Frontier, Richard Dunlop, Doubleday, 1962, pp. 161-162

Annals of Wyoming, "Army Life on the Wyoming Frontier," Alice Shields, Oct. 1941, Vol. 13, No. 4, p. 332

Colorado Gazetteer, 1871, Denver Public Library

Rocky Mountain West, Louis L. Simonin, University of Nebraska, 1966, p. 33

An Army Boy of the Sixties, Maj. Alson B. Ostrander, World Book Co., New York, 1924, pp. 232-235

trimmings. Numerous Chinese were available to help us carry our bundles to the hotel.

The highlight of the two day visit was a trip to the racetrack. Charles was impressed with the quality of the horses displayed.

Our trip home seemed more pleasant as we recalled the excitement of exploring a big city. The train engineer also added to our amusement on the trip home by racing with a small herd of antelope. This sport thrilled most of the travelers to the verge of hysterics.

Union Pacific Station and Hotel in Cheyenne 1869. *Courtesy of Union Pacific Railroad Museum Collection.*

December 1870

Dear Diary,

We are three days out from Fort D. A. Russell. I find traveling with a Quartermaster Army train both unusual and exciting. The train is made up of thirty Army wagons "laden with various kinds of freight and drawn by government mules. Usually several of the outfits travel together, sometimes with a Cavalry escort from the Fort." In this case we are fortunate to have Charles' Infantry Company with us. I am the only female on this journey and every soldier feels it his duty to watch and guard me. All of this attention flatters me, but leaves me little time for private matters.

The Army mules have proved a revelation to me. They are such superb animals and have an abundance of energy. One of the soldiers told me, "when new mules are purchased for transportation purposes in the Army, their tails are promptly shaved of all hair. This distinguishes them from the old, trained, experienced animals and renders it easy to pick them out of the herd when necessary. By the time the hair has grown back on the tails, they are thoroughly broken to their new environment and duties. Their tails are never shaved again. Hence the name shavetail for a green young officer, new to the life."

Another source of amazement to me is the skill of the Army teamster. He speaks to each mule in dreadful curses. "I had never heard or conceived of any oaths like those. They made my blood fairly curdle." Charles explained that swearing was necessary in order to persuade the mules to accomplish their tasks.

The first night the soldiers saw to my needs, bringing wood and laying a small fire in the stove at the back of the ambulance. A small amount of hay was put under the buffalo skins, to make a snug bed for baby and me. Between trunks, bundles, stove, and bed there was no room to move.

The men attempted to set up tents, but ended up sleeping under the wagons. The violent wind was uncooperative.

The next morning we headed out on a flat, open plain. The wagons appeared snakelike as they made their way toward a ranch. The ranch was equipped for travelers. I was ushered into the main room where a fire was roaring. Baby and I warmed ourselves. "A basin and a pitcher awaited us, with soap and a towel that turns without end

Pioneering in the 70's, Mrs. George A. Gillard, unpublished manuscript, Wyoming State Archives, MSS 33A, p. 1

Random Recollections of An Army Surgeon, George J. Newgarden, Manuscript MSB 141, History of Medicine Division, National Library of Medicine, Washington, D. C., p. 4

The Gentle Tamers-Women of the Old West, Dee Brown, University of Nebraska Press, 1958, p. 45

The Rocky Mountain West in 1867, Louis Simonin, University of Nebraska Press, 1966

around a roller. I found mirrors, combs, brushes of all kinds, even toothbrushes, fastened by a long string so that everyone may help himself and no one can carry it off."

I did enjoy the security of sleeping under a solid roof, but I prefer the privacy of the Army ambulance. Traveling Army style is difficult and dirty. If I did not travel with Charles, I would be forced to remain behind like the other wives chose to do. Charles and I are intent on keeping our family together, whenever possible.

Old type "Army Wagon," six mule, jerk line, and is the old time freighter wagon. Courtesy of Wyoming State Archives.

Dear Diary,

After fifteen days with the Army wagon train, we arrived at Fort Fetterman. "The Officers and their families were out on their porches to welcome the new arrivals, it being quite an event in that forlorn country." They were also pleased with the new supplies the train brought.

Within a day's time we were comfortably settled in our new surroundings. All of the women at the Post helped me unpack and passed the day with pleasantries.

I questioned my new found friends as to the origin of the Post. They informed me that it had been established in 1867 and named after a vallant soldier, Captain William Judd Fetterman. The story surrounding this officer interested me, because a routine wood hauling detachment duty turned into such a disaster.

Capt. Fetterman took eighty-one men from the 18th Infantry and Second Cavalry at Fort Phil Kearny, out on the slopes of the Big Horn Mountains to come to the assistance of a wagon train hauling wood. This train had been attacked by Indians. "Goaded on by decoys, the eighty-one men were lured into an ambush of two thousand Sioux, Cheyenne, and Arapaho Indians, and all were slain." Some of the bodies were recovered and returned to the Fort. By nightfall the Indians surrounded Fort Kearny which was undermanned and lacking in ammunition. Col. Henry B. Carrington asked for a volunteer who would ride to the closest fort for reinforcements. John Phillips, a civilian Quartermaster employee nicknamed "Portugee," offered to go on the condition that he could take the Colonel's thoroughbred horse. With the condition met, he set off on the 236 mile ride to Fort Laramie.

With the messenger on his way, Col. Carrington directed the men to set up three lines of defense. The first was the stockade; the second was a series of wagons that were turned sides up surrounding the magazine; and the last was the magazine. Ten women and several children were told that as soon as the Indians made their attack, they should go into the magazine. The plan was that if the men could not hold, the magazine and all its occupants would be blown up—saving them from the savages.

Random Recollections of An Army Surgeon, George J. Newgarden, Manuscript MSB 141, History of Medicine Division, National Library of Medicine, Washington, D. C.

John Portugee Phillips, R. R. Larson, MSS 587, Wyoming State Archives, p. 1
Ibid., p. 4

John Phillip's long ride was a tale all in itself. Fighting a blizzard and −22° temperature, he had to allude the Indians by traveling at night and hiding in the day. His food supply gave out on the second day. His incredible sense of direction even under these conditions, brought him to Fort Laramie. He arrived "with icicles hanging from his clothing, snow and ice matting his black, pointed beard, staggering from exhaustion and exposure . . ."

Reinforcements and supplies were sent to Fort Kearny and the episode called the Fetterman Massacre was brought to an end.

When I realize how recently these events were and how safe our life was at Fort D. A. Russell, I feel ashamed about my concern over things of little matter.

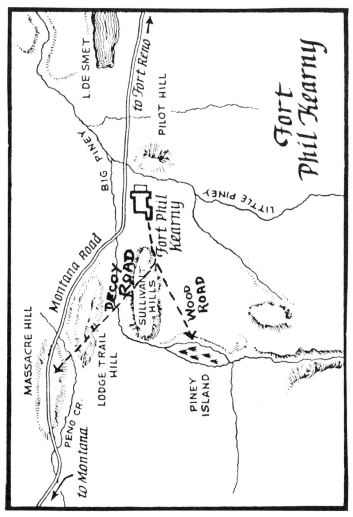

Map taken from *Fort Phil Kearney An American Saga*, Dee Brown, G. P. Putnam's Sons, New York, 1962.

37

Dear Diary,

I just received a letter from Mrs. Rogers at Fort D. A. Russell. What a pleasure it is to hear some news from friends. A piece of my heart remains at our first military home there.

She mentioned that General John D. Stevenson was discharged from the Army the end of December. He was the first Post Commander at Fort Russell from 1867-1868 and after that was assigned to Fort Fred Steele. He was a striking character who stirred much controversy among those who served under him.

General Stevenson was "a man who in those early days by his liberal interpretation of the powers with which he was vested, by his generosity and fine soldierly qualities, did much to assist the founders and early pioneers of the "magic city" in their gallant efforts to enforce law and order in the new town." He served the town as an official greeter to incoming guests such as foreign visitors and groups like the Rocky Mountain Excursionists.

Stevenson was quick to invest in lots in the new city. He purchased Lots 19 and 20 of Block 416 from the Union Pacific Railroad Company, on September 14, 1867. Town lots measured 66x132 feet and were sold by the U.P. for $150. Only one-third cash was required. Within thirty days afterward, they sold for $1,000 cash, and in two to three months the same lots were in demand from $2,000 to $2,500. Most lots were purchased by investors who put only a part of the selling price down. Some were purchased by citizens who spent their entire savings. In many towns laid out by the Union Pacific, the town died after the railroad moved on. Cheyenne seems to have survived but presumably the U. P.'s free use of the nearby Army at Fort Russell to remove squatters and to maintain law and order, stabilized the town during and after the departure of the railroad crews.

During the month of October 1867, General Stevenson erected a massive stone warehouse in Cheyenne, 80 x 120 feet, the walls being two feet thick, at a cost of about $20,000. Later that year a "terrible wind storm came upon the city from the northwest and tore the roof from the warehouse and did considerable damage." This warehouse was

---

Post Returns, Roll 1050, Microfilm 617, F. E. Warren A.F.B. Museum, Jan. 1871

Annals of Wyoming, "History of Wyoming," C. G. Coutant, 14:2, p. 153

Cheyenne Leader, 15 October 1867, Wyoming State Archives

Laramie County Clerk, General Index, Contract B, p. 20, microfilm 16, Wyoming State Archives

History and Business Directory of Cheyenne, Feb. 1868, p. 29, Wyoming State Archives, pp. 15 and 29

J. D. Stevenson A.C.P. File, Record Group 94, Box 417, National Archives

constructed so that cars enter and deposit freight from the track, without the expense of carting.

At Fort D. A. Russell his influence was strongly felt. He established the new Post with a firm hand. He felt no qualms in asking the Army for anything he wanted, although many of his requisitions were refused as having insufficient justification. He was resourceful in providing for the needs of the garrison, although his methods were sometimes questionable.

I remember how disgusted Capt. J. S. Tomkins was after he loaned General Stevenson $1,000 in September of 1867 and to my knowledge it has not been repayed yet. Tomkins sent many letters including one to the Adjutant General enlisting the Army's help in regaining the money. I do not know for what purpose the money was used, but some of his business ventures required great funding. It seems to me he was negligent in this matter.

Many people, including Reverend Cook of Cheyenne, expressed intense relief when he was moved to another post and a new Post Commander arrived at Fort Russell. Whatever his strengths and weaknesses, it appears the Army has discharged a "colorful" soldier.

General John D. Stevenson: First Post Commander, Fort D. A. Russell. *Courtesy of Wyoming State Archives.*

Dear Diary,

This Post is so far from anything, that the coming of a lone rider creates excitement for all. Two days ago, one of the ladies here had a surprise visit from her father. This evening, Charles and I invited him for a light dinner and some interesting talk. He was a sea captain, who in his younger days, used to sail his ship around the Horn, bringing cargo, emigrants, and sometimes soldiers, to the California coast. On these trips, he would stop for food or supplies in countries on the South American coast. He told us stories of "women and children kneeling in prayer in the streets before ancient churches, the fierce battling of the game cocks, padres playing cards, and meat cut into strips and sold by the yard, (while) calico was sold by the pound." These strange tales brought more questions from both Charles and me. Soon, as we moved out into the cool night air, the other Officers and their wives joined in, all sitting around the old man listening to his stories like young children. They almost seemed like fairy tales.

Then he brought us back to reality by describing the horrors of illness on board a ship. Since the ship was built for transporting cargo, the addition of passengers made for cramped space and health problems. Turbulent seas, and high winds brought the passengers to their knees. Sea sickness was common. Where scurvy and constipation was common among the crews on such long voyages, now the passengers brought aboard smallpox and cholera. When smallpox hit his men, he went into port and sent up the distress signal. A doctor would be sent out. In each port of call the doctors would take a look, leave sulphur, a pint of carbolic acid and some bailey, and then leave the ship as quickly as possible. Many times the captain buried his men at sea. He then told us of a book that had been his 'Bible' during his voyages—*The Seaman's Medical Guide.* He had bought it in Boston before leaving the States. He told us that without a doctor on board, this book had served to describe diseases, and give suggestions as to possible cures. It saved some lives and now he uses it as he travels west.

There was no doubt in my mind that he had faced many problems that I too, had met at this Post so far from civilization. One of the more comical experiences he related was concerning drinking water. Heaven knows, that has been a part of our problems too. The problem was to preserve the water on such long voyages. Sometimes small amounts of "quicklime, calcined lime, pure charcoal and muriatic or sulphuric acid" was poured into the barrels. "It may not have had any effect in

---

Doctors of the American Frontier by Richard Dunlop, Doubleday, 1962, pp. 114, 109

preserving the water, (he said) but it certainly had some in preventing the decay of the casks." And just think how it must have helped their digestion!

At this point, the conversation turned toward the ears of the men only. We ladies excused ourselves, and continued our "women talk" in the kitchen. It turned out to be a most pleasant evening and a welcome break from the monotony of post life.

Dear Diary,

What a pleasure it is to be back in civilization again! After eleven months at Fort Fetterman, Cheyenne and Fort D. A. Russell seem like an oasis on the plains. The advantages of living near a town and the railroad, became evident during our short stay at a real frontier outpost.

Charles' change in station could not have come at a more delightful time, as the holiday season is just beginning.

We moved into quarters with 2nd Lt. Thaddeus Capron and his family. William is now a year and a half old, walking, and enjoys the company of the Capron's children. The freedom of a secure home and surroundings, permit all the children to play without need of constant parental supervision. The confinement of two families living in one set of quarters does not strain as it did before. Perhaps it is because I am now also a seasoned Army wife.

Preparing a large meal for Thanksgiving is so easy here. All the ingredients are available within easy distance. Mrs. Capron and I marketed at I. C. Whipple's Grocers, west of the post office, in Cheyenne yesterday. The hams were plentiful but the price seemed a little high at twenty-five cents a pound. To celebrate our return to the Post, we shared the cost of one large smoked ham.

From the Subsistence Officer we received some turnips, potatoes, sugar, flour, and cheese. Mrs. Capron laughed because the turnips were from the same shipment that arrived the year past. It seems the abundance of turnips has led to a distaste for their sight.

We fed the children before our company arrived. We have only adequate seating for eight. They especially enjoyed the Indian Pudding. Single Infantry Officers were our guests and their appetites amazed me.

My contribution to the dinner was a recipe I got while at Fort Fetterman. Due to the lack of fresh eggs and dairy products, we women had to improvise on recipes. One of these was an "Apple Pie Without Apples."

After dinner conversation was brief as the men wanted to pay holiday greetings to their friend Pat Hannifan. It was sometime later that I realized what all the wives at the Post already new. "A multitude

---

Post Returns, Microfilm 617, Roll 1050, November 1871, Warren A.F.B., Museum Study Room

Cheyenne Leader, May 1871, Wyoming State Archives

Letters of the Subsistence Officer, 1869-1871, p. 32, Record Group 393 National Archives

Early History of Cheyenne, H. L. Kuykendall, unpublished manuscript, Wyoming State Archives, MSS 443, p. 5

Recipes: Indian Pudding—*Pioneer Potluck,* p. 24, Colorado Historical Society; Apple Pie—*American Heritage,* April 1964, p. 114

of saloons (existed); one of the most famous was 'Red Pats'. This saloon had the patronage or was the haunt of the soldiers stationed at Fort Russell and Camp Carlin. It took a man of untold nerve and fighting ability to conduct that place in anything like an orderly manner but fortunately it had the right man in the right place as Pat Hannifan knew no fear and was a nonpareil at the Rough and Tumble game."

Charles was thus reacquainted with the local amusements and I to the distractions of civilization.

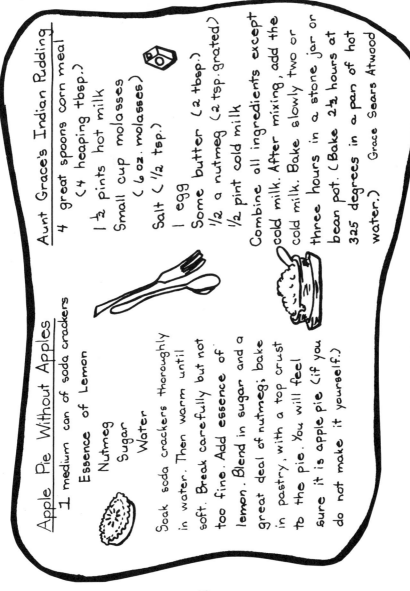

Aunt Grace's Indian Pudding

4 great spoons corn meal (4 heaping tbsp.)
1½ pints hot milk
Small cup molasses (6 oz. molasses)
Salt (½ tsp.)
1 egg
Some butter (2 tbsp.)
½ a nutmeg (2 tsp. grated)
½ pint cold milk

Combine all ingredients except cold milk. After mixing, add the cold milk. Bake slowly two or three hours in a stone jar or bean pot. (Bake 2½ hours at 325 degrees in a pan of hot water.)   Grace Sears Atwood

Apple Pie Without Apples

1 medium can of soda crackers
Essence of Lemon
Nutmeg
Sugar
Water

Soak soda crackers thoroughly in water. Then warm until soft. Break carefully but not too fine. Add essence of lemon. Blend in sugar and a great deal of nutmeg; bake in pastry, with a top crust to the pie. You will feel sure it is apple pie (if you do not make it yourself.)

Dear Diary,

The weather has been so severe that the trains are in from the West for the first time in fifteen days. They have been delayed by the deep snowdrifts. The news of men freezing on the range is heard frequently.

We had a reminder here at Fort D. A. Russell of how dangerous it can be to be exposed to the elements. A recruit from the 5th Cavalry named Kirby, left the recruit train at its first stop west. When he returned the train had left without him. When a second train came along heading East toward the Fort, he boarded it. The conductor soon forced him off because of the problem with tramps and bums riding the trains. Kirby could not prove he had been assigned to the 5th Cavalry. He walked all day and arrived Saturday with frozen fingers and toes. The poor fellow lost one big toe and the top portions of all of his fingers. Dr. Monroe was able to save his thumbs. Frostbite has been a problem all month among the troops. I've had enough of snow and the Wyoming winter to suffice the whole year.

Paymaster Clarke arrived this month. Charles' pay as a 2nd Lt. in the Infantry is $115.00 a month or $1400.00 a year. This pay is much less than he could earn even as a laborer in Cheyenne; but the Army is a way of life, and Charles has chosen it. At Fort Fetterman I had no trouble saving a bit as there was no place to spend it. Here however, the temptations of the city plague my budget.

The social event of the month was the visit on January 17th of the Grand Duke Alexis and party. He is a descendent of the Imperial Family of Russia. It is fashionable, now that the transcontinental railroad is completed, to have visitors from foreign countries passing through Cheyenne. Sightseeing and investment opportunities attract not only nobility, but anyone with money.

The train carrying the distinguished visitor and General Sheridan and staff, arrived at Cheyenne in the morning. The Officers of the Post and the Post Band were at the Depot to greet them. The band played throughout the layover even though the cold bit through to the bone. When the train slowly departed, the last car ran off the track. It was occupied by General Sheridan. Some time was needed to replace the car. The rest of the train went on to Denver and General Sheridan and his staff paid an unexpected visit to the Post for lunch. He was not put out by the inconvenience to his schedule, and impressed us all with his

---

Medical History of the Post, Microfilm H-62, Wyoming State Archives, Jan. 14, 1872, p. 249

Ibid. Feb. 3, 1872

Frontier Regulars, Robert M. Utley, Macmillian War Series, 1973, p. 20

Op. Cit. *Medical History of the Post*, January 17, 1872

Cheyenne Leader, 17 January 1872, Wyoming State Archives

distinguished look, and even temperament.

After several hours, he was escorted to the Depot where he and his entourage departed. The Post women are still talking of his stopover, and their surprise at meeting the Commander of the Division of the Missouri. Everyone at the Post has benefited from the change in conversation. The harshness of the winter paled in relation to the excitement surrounding General Sheridan's visit.

Courtesy of Union Pacific Railroad Museum Collection.

Dear Diary,

The report of a major scandal has just been released in many newspapers. I am set aback and so grateful that none of our meager monies were invested in a venture such as this. Charles says that some Army men stationed at forts in southwestern Wyoming, did have first hand experience in meeting the swindlers and their victims.

It seems that some prospectors named Phillip Arnold and John Slack, went to Table Rock at the head of Ruby Gulch and "salted the mesa with precious stones procured in Holland; then they took interested persons to the place, blindfolded, to see their great discovery." The *San Francisco Chronicle* reported the diamonds were brought originally from the Cape of Good Hope. Nobody is sure where they really did come from.

Rumors spread even to the continent of Europe where great speculation took place about the newly discovered diamond field in America. Diamonds were to be found merely by kicking up anthills. Rubies, sapphires, and emeralds were also discovered on this plateau, heretofore "an association impossible in nature."

Samples were sent to Tiffany in New York for study and his esteemed judgement presented in a special report. The report declared very high values in the lots sent to him. Speculators the world over, clammered to invest in the profitable venture. A group of investors were finally taken to the diamond field through a round about course south of the Union Pacific line. The hunt for diamonds commenced immediately upon their arrival. Precious stones were found everywhere and the vision of unlimited wealth lit the eyes of everyone there.

Such famous people as Horace Greeley, Tiffany, and Baron Rothchild provided more than $500,000 for a promotion company. The company was organized in California entitled 'The San Francisco and New York Mining and Commercial Company.' Its designs were not only the mining of the precious stones but their preparation for the commercial market. Financial geniuses jumped willingly into the shares of this company and the value of the shares increased swiftly. The bulk of the shares were sold to men of established wealth. It is estimated

---

Wyoming: A Guide to Its History, Highways and People, W.P.A. Writer's Project, Oxford University Press, New York, 1941, p. 243

The Great Diamond Hoax, Asbury Harpending, University of Oklahoma Press, Norman, 1958, pp. 138-195

"The Diamond Hoax," Verticle File, Wyoming State Archives

that close to $880,000 was amassed by the scoundrels Arnold and Slack.

A geologist named Clarence King, determined to have a look at the field. After a close examination by a German friend and himself, a stone plainly containing the marks of the lapidary's tool was found. "This is the bulliest diamond field as never vas. It not only produces diamonds, but cuts them moreover also." (sic)

Word was sent back to the San Francisco Company, the fraud revealed, and the short lived dream for many would-be diamond millionaires came to a close.

Although I do wish occasionally for more adequate pay in the Army, I am thankful that we are not a part of the many people in the States today, who are totally absorbed in exploitation and financial attainment. There is no such thing as easy money. Dreams are good to have, but only hard work makes them come true.

Dear Diary,

This has been a bad summer for our garden. All of my time spent nursing the vegetable plants was for naught. Grasshoppers plagued most of Wyoming Territory, and the State of Nebraska. They destroyed what little green Fort D. A. Russell had. ". . . the afternoon looked very queer, and in a little while it became perfectly dark. The sky was obscured by grasshoppers. They came in great clouds and ate everything in their passage. We all had vines over our porches, and not a leaf was left . . . They were all night and the whole of the next day in passing." They slipped into every conceivable place. Even our home was overwhelmed by these horrible pests.

Since May, grasshoppers were not the only invaders. There has been considerable doubling up and overcrowding here at the Post. Most of the Officers of the marching companies, left their families here for the summer. Even the men of the 14th Infantry who have been assigned to Fort Laramie, have retained quarters here, "adding much to the general embarrassment." Our former house-mate, Capt. Chambers has returned also, wearing the new rank of Major.

We have been watching with great interest the progress in the drilling of an artesian well. A first well was attempted during our absence from Fort D. A. Russell. It was unsuccessful, "having caved in and injured its tubing to such a degree that it was considered cheaper to begin a new well than to attempt to sink the first deeper." The well engineer is dubious of successful results in this unexplored soil. Hauling water for Post needs is a difficult task summer and winter and this well would solve the need for a continuous supply of unfailing good water.

Charles had some Infantry Officers over for a game of "whist." The talk revolved around the cramped conditions at the Post and the news of the Supreme Court decision against the Union Pacific Railroad Company. Charles explained to me that the State of Nebraska brought suit against the railroad for non-payment of property taxes. The original case came to court in Lincoln County, Nebraska in 1871. The

---

History of Wyoming, T. A. Larson, Univ. of Nebraska Press, 1965, p. 108

Reminiscences of a Soldier's Wife, Ellen McGowan Biddle, J. B. Lippincott Co., Phil., 1907, p. 123

Medical History of the Post, Microfilm H-62, Wyoming State Archives, May 1873, p. 121

Reports of the Quartermaster General, Serial Sets D 1594: 1873-1873, and D 1635: 1874-1875, Wyoming State Library

Op. Cit., *History of Wyoming*, p. 110

Case of U.P.R.R. verses Peniston, Cases Argued and Adjudged in the Supreme Court of the United States in U.S. Reports No. 85, October 1873, p. 5

circuit court found in favor of the State of Nebraska. The Union Pacific Company felt that they were a legitimate agency of the Federal Government, and therefore exempt from State or Territorial taxation. They in turn appealed to the United States Supreme Court. There had been much speculation in regard to the outcome of the case. Governor John Campbell says that Wyoming Territory will benefit from the decision. "Wyoming will be able to collect about one-third of its property taxes from the Union Pacific right-of-way, track, and rolling stock." Charles said that 'this is the first time any of the three giants, the Union Pacific, the Military, and the Government, have failed to scratch each other's back.' With the completion of the railroad and politicians living in Washington, I wonder who will be the defender of the military if a need arises.

FEDERAL LAND GRANTS FOR RAILROADS

LAND GRANT LIMITS
The shading shows the approximate limits of the areas in which the railroads received their land grants

ACREAGE GRANTED
The shaded areas are in proportion to the acreage received by the railroads. They do not show the exact location of the granted lands, which in general formed a checkerboard pattern.

Bureau of Land Management

Map taken from *History of Public Land Development,* Paul W. Gates, November 1868, p. 344.

49

December 1874

Dear Diary,

Fort D. A. Russell has been consumed these last few months with its own problems. The most frightening to me, is the dreaded scarlet fever that has hit the Post. In August the post surgeon ordered the laundresses quarters to be temporarily vacated so that they could be disinfected. Acid fumes were burned to destroy the scourge. Later the walls were whitewashed. I find myself keeping William isolated in the house for fear of contracting the "child killer." Most of the other mothers are following the same course.

The exterior silence is broken by sounds from the Post Hospital, where extensive repairs are being undertaken. The hospital structure has never been adequate. Dr. O'Reilly anticipates some small relief from the winter storms through these costly improvements.

I heard of the most unfortunate accident that befell Dr. O'Reilly. Upon coming from town in a buggy, he turned the corner at the Post Trader's store whereupon two dogs ran in front of the horses causing a runaway. The buggy overturned and Dr. O'Reilly "was very much injured with contusions." The problem with stray dogs has become so intolerable that a General Order was issued on the Post:

> "Persons owning dogs in this garrison are required to keep them on their own premises. On and after the 14th all loose dogs about the garrison will under the direction of the Officer of the Day, be killed."

The hopes of improving the sanitary problems surrounding our drinking water were halted abruptly with the abandonment of the sinking of an artesian well last spring. The Post drinking water comes from Crow Creek "which is now very low and quantities of shiny and vegetable matter, are deposited from its waters." As a result there have been a great number of cases of acute diarrhea caused by the impure water. The post surgeon has suggested we boil and strain our drinking water through cheesecloth. Our water barrels have been moved into the kitchen to hinder the constant freezing and thawing. Water is brought daily in large wagons to replenish the family quarters. In this severely cold weather, the men take refuge in our household to thaw themselves out. I do not envy them their difficult job.

I am busy making preparations for the holiday season. All sixteen

Post Surgeon's Report, Microfilm H-62, Wyoming State Archives, Vol. II, August 1874, p. 165

Ibid., Vol. II, December 16, 1874, page 185

General Orders, Fort D. A. Russell, #12, 12 March 1874, National Archives, Record Group 393

U.S. Congress (43rd) 2nd Session, Serial Set #D1635, 1874-1875, p. 182

Officers and their families are planning an evening of merriment together. I have some reservations about gatherings, especially now with so many health problems upon us.

March 1875

Dear Diary,

Last week I had a most thrilling experience which still leaves me shivering when I think of it. While passing the McDaniels Variety Theatre in Cheyenne, who should be departing but a gentleman of perfect form. He lifted his hat graciously and as he did, long, blond, silken curls descended to his shoulder-revealing none other than "Wild Bill" Hickok himself. I felt my nerves at loose ends but could not suppress my curiosity of this man. His presence in Cheyenne was a known topic of conversation during the last year, but my surprise at actually seeing him left me dumbfounded.

I gathered my wits and scrutinized every detail of him. He was fashionably dressed in the river boat gambler style with black and white, long tail, cutaway coat. His white pleated shirt shown from under a silk white vest with embroidered flowers. His patent leather boots gleamed beneath his checkered pants. His slim white hands and small feet seemed inadequate to serve a man of such stature. He was over six feet tall and weighed at least 200 pounds. A yellow mustache sat proudly beneath his "acquiline nose." His blue-gray eyes looked questioningly at me as we passed. I feared my curiosity had been too undisguised.

Upon my arrival back at the Post, I chattered uninterrupted for several minutes, to the neighbors who were gathered with Charles on our porch. They seemed entranced during my parley. Then they began telling me some fascinating tales about this gunfighter whose reputation preceded him even to the States.

It seems that at one time he was a member of one of "Buffalo Bill" Cody's melodrama shows. Rumor has it that he lost his taste for the theatrical, and rigorously avoids any reminder of his former trade. His love of gambling and card-playing has served to amuse him; although many of his fights have erupted from this circumstance. It is said that he goes easily against society for his own benefit, and "no one will vouchsafe that he was not dangerous-especially when drunk, mad, angry, and or jealous."

Different accounts say that thirty-five to eighty-five men have met their end with "Wild Bill." A well known saying is, "Stranger, stay shy o' that there Wild Bill Hickok. Specially when he's drunk as a skunk. Why, he's killed eighty-five men, not countin' Mexicans and Indians!"

The Bad Men of the West, George D. Hendricks, The Naylor Co., San Antonio, Texas, 1942, pp. 5, 68, 92, 93, 217

Wild Bill Hickok, Richard O'Connor, Curtis Books, New York, 1959, pages 198-210

The Gunfighters, Lea F. McCarty, Studio, Santa Rosa, California, 1959, p. 6

He is reported to have a certain "mania for emptying his six gun contents into the second O in a "saloon" from one hundred yards away."

His time in Cheyenne appears to have been relatively quiet and it is speculated by many that his eye sight has failed to such a point, that he couldn't hit a target if he tried. The Post Surgeon has examined his eyes and feels there is nothing that can be done without a trip East to a specialist. He is also afflicted with rheumatism. He appears not to have lost his courage but his ability instead. I wonder if it will be his undoing.

I can't help but fancy the day when William is old enough that I can relate the events of the day that I saw "Wild Bill" Hickok. I fear my relatives in the East would be appalled at my pluck!

"Wild Bill" Hickok arrived in Cheyenne in the fall of 1874 and remained here until early 1876. *Courtesy of Wyoming State Archives.*

Dear Diary,

Charles is still out with his Company. He will be surprised when he returns and sees the many changes which have taken place during the summer.

For most of the summer only two companies have been stationed at Fort D. A. Russell. Since July all of the men have been employed "as mechanics and laborers in the Quartermaster Department repairing the Officers' Quarters which have been plastered throughout, floors renewed where needed, rendering them much more comfortable and habitable than they have ever been. The out buildings are now undergoing repairs, water closets are being moved over, new pits dug for the purpose, and the old one filled in with earth." The mess rooms and kitchens of the soldiers' barracks were condemned by a board of Officers and pulled down. At present the men are eating in the lower room of the barracks.

Surgeon Randolph, through his recommendations, has encouraged more humane treatment for the prisoners confined in the guard house. He has suggested that "bedsacks filled with straw and a pillow tick similarly filled be provided for each cell; or that company commanders may be required to furnish them for their men when confined in the Guard House." Change of straw will be issued monthly. He reports that the blankets are seldom washed although they are beaten occasionally. He is concerned with the effects of cold, damp, air and foul odors upon the human body. Prisoners complain that the bedsacks are too short "and no amount of too short bed can make a man comfortable." Although I agree with our Post Surgeon, I know Charles would think it presumptuous of a medical man to interfere in the area of military discipline.

My mind has been preoccupied with the increasing number of skirmishes with Indians throughout the Territory. The Post is empty as it has been since May. Rumors of wounded troops reach the Post daily, and play on the nerves of all the women here Thank goodness for William who keeps my days full and provides me companionship. Even the children have reacted to rumors by playing games of soldiers and hostiles. I shall be relieved when Charles returns safely.

The summer was shadowed with the shocking news of Col.

Post Surgeon's Report, Microfilm H-62, Wyoming State Archives, Vol. II, page 215, October 1875.

Ibid., page 216

Circular No. 8, 1875, page 18, Surgeon General's Office, Medical Dept. of the Army.

Cheyenne Leader, 2 July 1875, Wyoming State Archives

Post Surgeon's Report, op. cit., page 218, December 1875

Carling's suicide. I do not know the circumstances surrounding his death, but in times like these the pressure on an army officer must be overwhelming. Word was also just received of Chaplain Ragan's death. He had been on sick leave in Ohio since February and succumbed to the bronchitis which he contracted in the line of duty in this severe climate.

Waiting for the troops plagues me with all kinds of fears. I feel depressed and wish for the happier, carefree life of my army sisters in the East.

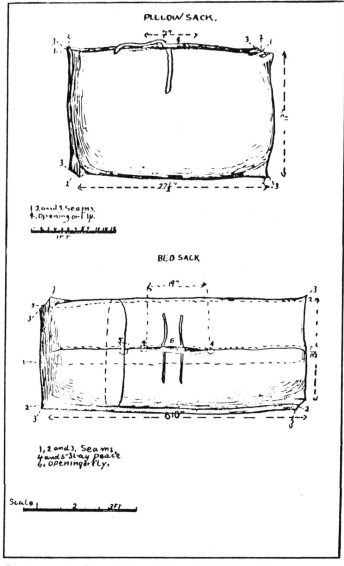

Quartermaster General Annual Report, 1884, p. 40.

July 1876

Dear Diary,

I must admit I have felt very upset these past weeks. It seems that the Army has a host of enemies; newspapers and magazines, as they arrive from the East, have all kinds of hideous stories about this Territory. It makes me wonder if I am in fact living in the same place. The attitude of Eastern society toward the Indian problem is most alarming. Humanitarians call the killing of Indian women and children "military butchery." They just do not understand the whole situation. The stories all seem to emphasize the number of noncombatants killed in military encounters. Politicians have chosen this as their major election issue and seem to be greatly influencing the thinking of their Eastern audience. The errand boys sent by them to follow the military troops as they encounter the Indians, see only the actions of the immediate moment and none of the long hours of consideration, discussion, and analysis prior to a decision.

Military men have diverse ideas on the Indian problems. When General Crook's cavalry returned to Fort D. A. Russell in late March, they were exhausted from their struggles with the savages. General Crook himself, feels that the use of Indian brother against brother within the same tribe is the only successful way of dealing with people who fail to see the obvious advantage of our civilization. Originally "it was the impulse to civilize the Indian that dominated military attitudes as it dominated public sentiment and government policy," not genocide. Because the Indians failed to obey the law requiring their return to the reservations, they have been turned into outlaws. At this point, officers began handling the enforcement of this law as their individual conscience directed them. Some concluded that "the confessed aim is to exterminate everyone, for this is the only advantage of making the expedition; if extermination were not achieved, just another burden would be added—prisoners." Some officers go to great lengths to distinguish between combatants and non-combatants. "In such encounters women and children are nearly always present. They mingle with the fighting men, often participate in the fighting, and in the confusion and excitement of battle are difficult to identify as noncombatants."

During these long summers when Charles is away, it is hard enough

Cheyenne Leader, March 1876, Wyoming State Archives
Frontier Regulars, Robert Utley, Macmillan, 1973, pages 52-53
An Army Doctor's Wife on the Frontier, Ed. Abe Laufe, University of Pittsburgh Press, 1962, page 309

to keep our spirits high; but when everyone in the East, even family, questions your moral code and belittle the reason Charles is putting his life in jeopardy, it becomes unbearable. I feel I have no allies except the other army women who share this burden. "This unsettled state of affairs will be the death of me yet."

Dear Diary,

The shock of this day is over but the memory of its events will remain with me forever. Dr. Patzki arrived at our home shortly after daybreak. He came with a duty to perform of which I was neither ready to hear nor was I aware that he would be such a messenger. He slowly explained the events of November 25th and as he spoke I suddenly realized that he was the bearer of dreadful news.

Charles' Company of the 23rd Infantry attacked a village near Sioux Pass of the Big Horn Mountains. "The village, consisting of one hundred and seventy-three lodges with their contents, was entirely destroyed, and about five hundred ponies were captured." The fight lasted for about an hour, but the skirmishes kept up until nightfall. In a very gallant charge upon the Indians, Charles was killed.

Lt. Col. Dodge, in command of the 23rd, allowed a small detachment to return to the Post by midweek. I watched the wagon move slowly toward the hospital; two of the men came to the house to pay their respects. I had trouble believing as well as really hearing all the words said and after they left, everything was strangely quiet. That night, after William was in bed, the silence was almost overpowering. I watched until the morning light hit our front window, and then the women were at my door, helping William and I get ready. They were most kind in their efforts, but it was only afterwards that I realized all they had done.

The procession left from the hospital where Reverend Jeremiah Porter said some words of comfort that I failed to hear. We all walked slowly to the cemetery behind the wagon. The whole garrison was attired in full dress uniform and the band kept up a steady pace. The snow was blown such, that drifts were piled against the other stones. The ground was hard under foot; such a cold place to lay to rest my dear husband.

After the service, the others headed back to the Post. William and I stayed on. It was William's tug at my sleeve that brought me out of my thoughts. I had stood there for a long while and the wind was starting to blow with a fierce whip. I don't remember much more of that day, except the kind Reverend's visit and the trip into Cheyenne where William and I took up our new residence. The women had packed the last of our things that morning and then piled them into an

---

Record of Engagements with Hostile Indians (1868-1882), Government Printing Office, 1882, pages 64-65

Reminiscences of a Soldier's Wife, Ellen McGowan Biddle, J. B. Lippincott Co., 1907, page 70

My Army Life and the Fort Phil Kearney Massacre, Frances C. Carrington, J. B. Lippincott, 1910, page 156

army wagon. "The nervous strain I was under, besides the trying climate, was fast telling on me." Dr. Patzki suggested a trip East but I did not have sufficient funds for such a journey.

That night, somewhat settled in our two rooms, I remembered my husband's locket. It "had a picture of myself in a choice setting that he always wore, and I . . . wondered what Indian Chief had it now in possession to wear as a trophy . . . of that desperate battle."

Dear Diary,

My first month in seclusion was broken by many sympathy calls. The men from Charles' company have returned from the Powder River Expedition and have been encamped near Fort D. A. Russell. Many have been most gracious in paying their respects to me. It comforted me to hear their remarks about Charles' fine qualities as an officer.

The company has been disappointed that they are unable to return to the Post and their families due to the smallpox quarantine. The disease is of epidemic proportions in Cheyenne and no one has been allowed to visit from the Fort. It seems that many of my military contacts were severed abruptly by the disease.

William continues to be my source of strength. He is now five years old and a blessing to ease my loneliness. I am over protective of him for fear of the disease; I couldn't stand to lose him too.

I have been watching with much interest, the court martial trial of General Joseph J. Reynolds. It is being held in the Inter-Ocean Hotel in Cheyenne. The Court consists of many well-known Generals. Charges were brought against Gen. Reynolds by General George Crook who was, at the time of the incident, commanding the entire Big Horn Expedition. At one point in March of 1876, they scouted a large Indian village on the Powder River. General Reynolds took three hundred men and raided the village. "The village was a perfect magazine of ammunition, war material, and general supplies, and every evidence was found to prove that Indians were in copartnership with those at the Red Cloud and Spotted Tail Agencies, and that the proceeds of raids upon the settlements had been taken into those agencies and supplies brought out in return." General Reynolds was charged with leaving the bodies of two soldiers, not capturing "Crazy Horse," and not obeying orders concerning supplies; the latter charge he did admit to.

It was brought out in the trial that Reynolds was unaware of the death of the two soldiers until later. "The command had suffered so much from the severity of the weather, the mercurial thermometer failing to register the intensity of the cold, that after the destruction of the village the column returned to Fort Fetterman . . ."

The finding of the Court Martial Board was a one year suspension

Medical History of the Post, Microfilm H-62, Wyoming State Archives, Vol. II, p. 242, January 1877

"My Life Story," James Flood Jenkins, unpublished manuscript No. MSS 47, Wyoming State Archives, pp. 26-29

Record of Engagements with Hostile Indians, Government Printing Office, Washington, 1882, pp. 50-57

Frontier Regulars, Robert Utley, Macmillan and Co., 1973, pp. 256, 258

on the one charge to which he admitted. It is rumored that President Grant, a long time friend of General Reynolds, will set the findings aside, and allow him to retire with all honors.

The troops who have visited with me seem to feel that "Crook had to clear his own skirts, so his attacks on General Reynolds were very bitter." They also believe Major Stanton, who accompanied General Crook, to be a "correspondent for some Eastern daily newspaper to write glowing achievements of the General." Perhaps the inquiries of the newspaper brought about a question which might otherwise have been overlooked.

General George Crook, Commander of the Big Horn Expedition. *Courtesy of Wyoming State Archives.*

November 1877

Dear Diary,

I had a visit from the Post Chaplain, who just returned from a three month leave. He was full of news of the East and of his family. Chaplain Porter comes from a family of well-educated people. His brother is Rev. Henry D. Porter, M.D. who is doing missionary work in northern China; his only daughter had just returned from spending nine years in China too, working with her Uncle. He described their happy family reunion.

He also gave me news of the Post. It was clear that he was very upset that the Officers and their families are now attending services in town. The Children's Sunday School held at 2 P.M. is only attended by a few of the soldier's children, and he asked me if I might like to have William join them. I was most pleased with the invitation, and accepted. I think he is looking to see me at his morning service too, but he did not say so.

He was most concerned with the increasing number of men in the Guard House for drinking. Last January, he was successful in getting forty-one soldiers to sign a "total abstenance pledge" (sic) but they have now reverted back to their old ways, without his encouragement and those Thursday night temperance meetings. We talked at great length about the enlisted men. He feels very strongly that the post trader should not sell liquor, but I told him that many of the men come into town, and get their drinks here. He asked me if I had any ideas on how to quiet their thirst, and I told him that they did not have any form of recreation and maybe that would help the situation. I think he is hoping that with the return of the troops and the Band playing at the evening service, the men will come to sing and that will be their recreation. He showed me a paper that the Post Library Association was printing specifically for the enlisted men. It is called "The Battles Flag" and I found it most dry—but of course I did not mention that to Chaplain Porter.

The rest of the visit was spent in asking me about my needs and how we were making out. I told him honestly, that we were just making ends meet. The sewing that I am doing and the kindness of the ladies at Fort D. A. Russell, make it possible for us to survive. When he asked about my health, it led us into an hours discourse on the health of his wife and himself. He had left Fort Sill for health reasons, and has found

A.C.P. File No. 74, Box 28, Record Group 94, National Archives, Letter dated November 16, 1878
    Ibid., Letter dated January 2, 1878
    Ibid., Letter dated January 31, 1877
    Ibid., Letter dated January 2, 1878

this part of the country to be good for his wife's malaria attacks, but not for his rheumatism.

After our visit, I think he felt better. I felt that the invitation to come to the Fort each Sunday would be lovely for me; while William is in Sunday School, I can visit with some of my friends. The Chaplain promised to send an ambulance around for me next Sunday, and I am looking forward to the event.

Dear Diary,

The entire Post is relating the story of the events of yesterday. It shocks me to think of the injustice man inflicts upon his neighbors. I am enclosing this clipping from the *Cheyenne Leader* to remind me that Cheyenne and the Fort are not as comfortably civilized as I should like to think.

FATAL STABBING AT FT. RUSSELL

"About 3 o'clock yesterday afternoon the sutler's store was the scene of a bloody affray in which James Murray, a soldier of Captain Payne's company, F. Fifth Cavalry, met his death at the hands of a worthless bummer named Edward Baker, a hanger-on at the company kitchen.

The facts of the homicide, as gleaned from eye-witnesses, are as follow:

Murray either owed or had promised to give Baker some money, and after the troops were paid off, yesterday, both men fell to drinking, and were soon intoxicated. Murray gave Baker money several times, and Baker as often spent it and asked for more. Baker then said:

"Then you're a s— of a—." Murray turned away saying:

"I'll take that from a baby, but I wouldn't from anyone else."

This angered Baker and he went into the store, bought a large knife, and rushing upon Murray, cut a severe gash in his forehead, and then plunged the gory blade into his heart.

Murray fell, and died within five minutes, speaking but a few words after being stabbed.

Baker was at once placed under arrest by Adjutant King, and is now confined in the guard-house at the Fort. On account of threats made by Murray's comrades, the guard was increased to thirty-six men, so that all danger of a necktie festival was averted.

Coroner Goldaker, on being notified, proceeded to the post and held an inquest over Murray's remains, the verdict being in accordance with the facts.

Murray was a veteran, being in the Fifth Cavalry for 22 years. He was about 50 years of age. His murderer has been in this section several years, and is widely known. He has respectable and prominent relatives in the states. He was a member of F company for about six months, but was discharged last spring, and has been living off the company most of the time since then."

The Cheyenne Leader, 12 December 1877, Wyoming State Archives

Graff 71

Courtesy of Everett D. Graff Collection, Newberry Library, Chicago.

65

Dear Diary,

A group of ladies from Fort D. A. Russell and myself went calling on the women at Camp Carlin. The one and a half mile ride was made in an army ambulance, although I have walked it many times in better weather. I enjoyed visiting with Mrs. Capron who had opened her home to us a few years ago when we returned from Fort Fetterman. Lt. Capron has since been assigned to duty at Camp Carlin. My son, William, and Elo Capron are great playmates. They withdrew to the nursery while the ladies gossiped with their tea.

The conversation centered on the forthcoming HOP to be held in the school hall on the twenty-second of this month. Mrs. Charles King, Mrs. Gerhardt Luhn, and Mrs. Rogers are in charge of decorating the hall. We talked about the possibilities of having cloth draped over the windows, and greens around the doorways. Tallow candles by the dozen set in tin reflectors will illuminate the hall. Although Mrs. Capron is not on the committee, her husband has access to certain supplies through the stores of the Quartermaster's Department. We refrained from specific requests, but hinted a great deal. We were all relieved when she offered to speak with her husband about borrowing the needed items.

The social life at Fort Russell is always first class. There are a total of sixteen officers and families, and four bachelors stationed here and at Carlin, who are hosting this affair. The Fifth Cavalry band, "the best in the United States," is to play for the dancing. Affairs of this sort are very important to both women and men; great excitement accompanies their preparation. One of the officers stopped me and said, "I am going to the Hop to see you dance, for I know if the floor were covered with eggs and you danced over them, not one would be broken." I became most flushed. It does seem to me that army women keep their youth because they dance so much. I do enjoy it and recall with pleasure the comment made to me by an older officer's wife. "You look as if a gentle wind would blow you over, yet you dance as you do; why you seem to possess more endurance than a government mule."

We have each prepared our contributions to the service of a

Thaddeus Hurlbut Capron Collection, #1694, Copy Book X, Hebard Room, University of Wyoming

Medical History of the Post, microfilm H-62, Wyoming State Archives, Vol. II, p. 262, December 1877

"Brief History of Fort D. A. Russell," *Kemmerer Camera,* dated 27 August 1919, Fort Warren File, Hebard Room, University of Wyoming.

Reminiscences of a Soldier's Wife, Ellen McGowan Biddle, J. P. Lippincott, 1907, pp. 49-50

beautiful table. I took great care in shining my silver service, and the little wine glasses and decanter set which are my prize possessions. Mrs. King is supplying the linen and Mrs. Rogers a delightful set of blue cups and saucers with Chinese figures on them.

I am remaking my party dress, adding fur trim from a muff that I dismantled. Fur trim is very stylish and I am hopeful that my new creation will receive notice. It is good for me to have such social projects to fill my time.

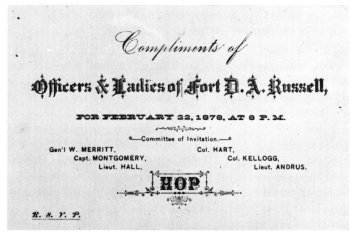

Courtesy of Western History Research Center, University of Wyoming.

Dear Diary,

It has been just over a year since I moved from Fort D. A. Russell into Cheyenne and it has been such a year of extremes.

When hot weather arrived, "the mosquito war began." "If the wind was in a certain direction, they tormented us all day long. I can see how" William and I must have looked taking our evening walk, with a scarf and overdress drawn over my head, "whisking handkerchiefs and beating the air with fans. It required constant activity to keep off the swarms of those wretched little insects that annoyed us every moment during our airing."

After William went to bed, my neighbor and I would sit on the porch after "wrapping newspapers around our ankles and feet, and drawing the stockings over, . . . tucking our skirts closely around us. We fixed ourselves in a chair, not daring to move . . . All vanity regarding personal appearance would be apt to disappear before the attacks to which we were subject." Strangers, unaccustomed to the mosquito onslaught, would beat "off the mosquitoes until there lay on the floor before them a black semicircle of those they had slain." We who were used to the seasonal attack would rather dress in layers than waste our time in warfare.

As the summer brought excessive amounts of mosquitoes, the winter has brought excessive amounts of snow. This week was high-lighted with an afternoon invitation to visit friends at the Post. Little did I know that my visit would turn into a two day stay. "A violent wind and snowstorm began. The storm raged with great violence, immense snowdrifts with columns of snow whirling through the air placed an insurmountable barrier to all communication in the garrison. So penetrating was the force of the wind that the snow was driven thru the houses on the flank exposed to its violence. Outdoors, objects a foot distant could not be discerned so inpregnable was the blinding mist of snow. The storm continued through the day and night with unabated vigor. Front and rear entrances to all buildings exposed to its force, were completely blockaded by drifts 6 to 10 ft. deep. The assertion may be safely ventured that the like is beyond the experience of the oldest inhabitant." The storm finally ended early the next day leaving drifts from 15 to 30 feet deep. A large force was employed tunneling and clearing drifts.

William and I made it back to Cheyenne the following day. I have

Boots and Saddles, Elizabeth B. Custer, University of Oklahoma Press, Norman, p. 152-153

Medical History of the Post, March 8 and 9, 1878, Vol. II, p. 265, Microfilm H-62, Wyoming State Archives

to admit that I enjoyed the stay and particularly the familiar feeling of enjoying a situation that might have otherwise been adverse. I still feel more comfortable with the army family than any other group. The army takes pride in caring for its own; for two days I received the benefit of this caring again.

Dear Diary,

I have made a difficult decision but one which I feel will enhance William's and my future. On Sunday next, I shall remarry.

I met him at St. Mark's Church at a box social. He honored me by purchasing my basket. We spent the afternoon in pleasant conversation. In late afternoon he escorted me home at which time he met William. I was flattered when he asked to call again.

I started thinking about him as a mate, as a father for William, and a provider. Life has not been easy since Charles' death. I have found it extremely hard to support William and myself on the meager funds which I receive for stitchery.

Although I didn't know it, he was looking for a mature, settled woman to be a companion. Life on the frontier is not to be faced alone. We both need the security of this union. By mutual agreement, because of the practical demands of life, we shall share our lot.

Richard is of English birth. His family is among the landed gentry although he will not be heir to inherit the family lands. He came to America seeking a new beginning and adventure. Like many foreign-born immigrants, the army offered an honorable way of life. The varieties of nationalities represented in the American army has always been of interest to me. In my experience about half of the men in the army are of foreign descent. Richard has a strong feeling of family importance and displays admirable fatherly qualities. His job with the army frees me from the anxiety of hostile engagements. He assures me that his duties as Subsistence Officer do not require his presence in the field. I feel William does not need to endure the loss of another father.

I look forward to moving back to the comfortable surroundings of Fort D. A. Russell. The quarters will be like those we lived in before. I shall renew old friendships and make new acquaintances. I have missed the social life at the post; towns-people were friendly, but there is always something special to me about army people. I think William looks forward to the move as much as me.

Although Richard's family will not be here, they already know of our plans, and I have received a letter from his Mother. It sounded warm and sincere in welcoming me to the family. I have not had immediate family for many years and feel excited at the prospect.

Fate has an interesting way of changing the direction of one's life. I hope I have made the right decision with what fate has given me.

Frontier Regulars, Robert Utley, Macmillan Press, 1973, p. 24

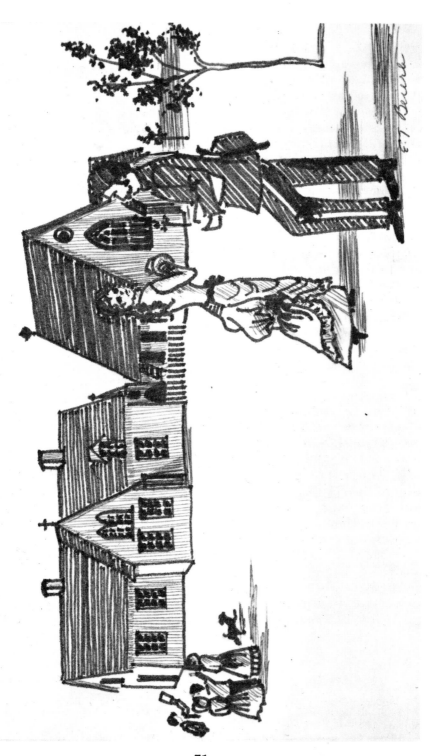

Dear Diary,

I am happily settled at Fort D. A. Russell again. It appears there will be many changes within the coming year. New buildings are being constructed by the troops on all sides of the Post.

Much to my surprise there is talk that the Army has lost the laundresses. Congress has voted to strike them from the rolls. Over twenty ladies here are affected by the decision. Many are married to enlisted men and need the rations provided as compensation.

In my limited experience at western posts, I have found two types of women that fill this position. The first type are women like Mrs. Smith who is the wife of a soldier and helped me during my time of confinement. She is a pleasant person, neat in appearance, and of sound moral character. She lives at the edge of the Post in temporary quarters, surrounded by the second type of laundress. These females live "amid squalor and children of dubious parentage (and) are objects of incessant attention and rivalry among the troopers." The Post Surgeons continually complain about the unsanitary conditions of their quarters and yards.

The original log and adobe temporary huts built in 1868 are still used by the laundresses and are totally unfit for man or beast. It is a shame. Plans are now under way for new Married Men's Quarters that were originally intended for them. At least those women married to soldiers will finally exchange their huts on Suds Row for new pine quarters.

Even the laundresses who remain at the Post will suffer by the new Congressional decision. Previously they received Army rations plus wages out of the troopers pay for their labors; the Army, considering them a necessity, permitted them to travel with the troops in the field. Because of the Army authorized designation they received housing, such as it was. Now they will lose the rations. They will lose the travel privilege. They will lose their houses. There is still a need for their services, however, so many will probably be able to earn some money.

One of the laundresses came to me in distress, feeling she would be unable to survive without the rations—she used them to feed her children.

The Army seems to feel laundresses cause more bother than they

Spurs to Glory, James M. Merrill, Rand McNally and Co., 1966, p. 178

Annals of Wyoming, "History of Fort Francis E. Warren," Jane Kendall, January 1946, Vol. 18, No. 1, p. 16

Frontier Regulars, Robert Utley, Macmillan Press, 1973, pp. 91-92

are worth. The ladies at the Post do not agree and feel they are a necessary part of living on a frontier post. Few of us know how to perform their duties for ourselves successfully. It appears I shall be forced to learn!

Married Mens' Quarters. Originally designed as laundresses' quarters. Constructed in 1879 at a cost of $196.00. *Fort D. A. Russell*, **Book 1**. *Courtesy of F.E. Warren A.F.B. Museum.*

October 1879

Dear Diary,

My heart sinks within me each time I hear the news of more Indian hostilities. I wonder if it will ever come to an end.

Reports have just come in stating that Major Thornburgh, along with nine enlisted men, have been killed by the savage Utes. Major Thornburgh left from Fort Fred Steele on September 21st at the request of the agent at White River Reservation, Mr. N. C. Meeker.

Richard read the report to the other officers. On the morning of September 29th, Major Thornburgh, with two troops of cavalry, had just turned off from the wagon train and was about a mile distant when he saw the first savages. Their attitude being hostile, the troops were deployed. At the same time however, Major Thornburgh and Lt. Cherry, Fifth Cavalry, attempted to communicate with the Indians. This was met by a volley from the hostiles and sharp engagement soon developed.

In unfavorable tactical terrain, and vastly outnumbered by a well-armed enemy with large amounts of ammunition, an orderly withdrawal to the main body of the wagons was begun. Major Thornburgh started for the wagons after ordering Captain Layson, Third Cavalry, to clear the knoll of savages who were attempting to block the withdrawal. He had just crossed the river and was within 500 yards of the train when he was shot and instantly killed.

The rest of the troops successfully reached the wagons and a bitter fight ensued the rest of the day and into the night. During a lull in the fighting, about midnight, water was obtained from the river and couriers were dispatched to the railroad to telegraph for help.

"As quickly as possible, after receipt of orders at Fort D. A. Russell, Col. Wesley Merritt, and troops from the Fifth Cavalry, were upon a special train for Rawlins, From this point, by a march of almost unparalled rapidity, in something over forty-eight hours, Col. Merritt's column, consisting of three hundred and fifty men, one hundred and thirty-one of whom were infantry following in wagons, marched one hundred and seventy miles over a most difficult road and reached the command at Milk River at half past five o'clock in the morning of October 5."

"It was found that the Indians had burned and utterly destroyed the agency, had killed the employes and the agent, Mr. Meeker, and had

Across the Country with the Fifth Cavalry, George F. Price, Antiquarian Press, Ltd., New York, 1959 (originally published in 1883 by D. Van Nostrand, New York)

Record of Engagements with Hostile Indians, Government Printing Office, Washington, 1882, pp. 88-92

carried off all the females into the horrors of savage captivity."

Thinking a general war with the Utes was coming, thousands of soldiers were hurried to Rawlins some of whom were with the Third Cavalry under Col. A. G. Brackett. Operations were suspended quickly however, when the Indian Department requested negotiations "with the Utes for release of the captive females and surrender of the ringleaders in the late outrages."

After Richard finished reading, the men spent the evening recalling their own encounters with Indians. I tired quickly of the conversation, feeling it a subject too personal to my own past. I continue to wonder, however, why the Indians refuse to accept our superior way of life. Their savagery and destruction go beyond the endurance of human patience.

Col. A. G. Brackett, Commander of Fort D. A. Russell from 1880-1882. *Courtesy of U.S. Signal Corps, Brady Collection, National Archives.*

November 1880

Dear Diary,

The storehouses are now full again. Last month, a company of the third cavalry returned from twenty-five days of hunting in the vicinity of Laramie Peak. They were very successful and the wagons arrived loaded with "37 elk, 150 antelopes, 3 mountain sheep, and a number of small game, such as Sage Hen etc." This week another company returned with many elk and deer. The troops will continue to be busy preparing the meat for our winter's use.

In addition to this, the entire garrison has been tasked with the responsibility of policing the Post for the upcoming inspection by the Inspector General of the Department of the Platte. The women were warned that they may be inspecting the quarters which makes us accountable for the condition of the building itself. I have been redding up for the past two weeks and even William is tiring of cleaning the grounds surrounding our quarters. The wind has been most uncooperative by constantly barraging us with more debris. If our prayers are answered, snow will fall before his arrival and the grounds will be one less thing to worry about. I wonder why my housekeeping ability would come under the perusal of the military. Richard, however, reminds me that I am an Army wife and it is expected of me.

Lt. Col. W. B. Royal inspected for three days and then left. Tension at the Post eased upon his departure and routine of daily garrison life returned.

More welcome visitors arrived at mid-month. "Two French Officers Lt. Col. Bon Faverot de Kernreck and Capt. Henry de La Chira of the 13th Dragons, visited the Post . . . for the purpose of inspecting the Cavalry Companies." This inspection was for the purpose of learning and incorporating the techniques used by the cavalry into the French military service. They were delightful, gentile officers, and I must admit the women here passed beyond the standard bounds of etiquette in meeting their comforts. Again they pooled their finest tableware for the four-day visit. Col. and Mrs. J. H. King entertained them in their quarters. Some of the newly killed game graced the meal.

Perhaps the most welcome visitor of the month was Major Towar, the paymaster. He arrived and paid the men for two months. It seems the Army is always behind in payments to the troops, but in this case it was well he arrived after the inspection!

Medical History of the Post, Microfilm H-62, Wyoming State Archives, October 1880, Vol. II, p. 333
Ibid., pp. 337-338

Dear Diary,

An order issued from the Headquarters of the Army, prohibits the sale of liquor by Post Traders on military reservations. It has met with much enthusiasm among the troops here at Fort D. A. Russell. A petition was circulated among the enlisted men and forwarded to the President of the United States, Garfield. The petition was signed by over two hundred enlisted men. I feel great pride in the quality of the enlisted men here, although the response among enlisted men may vary at other posts.

I read the entreaty in the March 10th issue of the *Cheyenne Leader* and found many interesting points concerning the sale of liquor on the Post. I was unaware that "the liquor provided for the officers, in quality, comes up to about the average standard of liquor sold in any well assorted and well stocked bar room; while . . . the liquor offered for sale to the enlisted men, is nothing but a vile chemical compound, containing, exclusive of a little alcohol, none of the ingredients of either whisky, brandy, or wine." It was stated that officers are sold liquors at a reasonable price, while the "liquor" sold to enlisted men is always sold at exhorbitant prices.

The men feel that the lack of discipline and necessity of court martials is aggravated by the sale of "spiritous liquor." "One drink of the average post trader's liquor sold to enlisted men, if it does not intoxicate, will at least so effect him as to render him unable to properly perform the duties required of him as a soldier." Excessive drinking is not necessary to result in this condition. Living without the normal social ties, the enlisted man finds himself prey to the temptation of drink. "The punishment, therefore, that the enlisted man suffers, the fines that he pays, the disgrace entailed upon him through incarceration, and his dishonorable discharge from the Army, are for the most part but the consequences of a drunken spree either begun or ended at the post trader's bar."

It is obvious that the soldiers resent the fact that the Post Trader, with only a minimal output, gains an income that enables him to live comfortably, off "of the degradation, debasement, and complete physical destruction of the enlisted man."

Richard feels that the prohibition of liquor at the Post Trader's store, is in the best interest of the Army, and moral conditions at the posts. We are both hopeful that the post traders will be unable to

Cheyenne Leader, March 10, 1881, Wyoming State Archives
The Holy Bible, King James Version, Isaiah 5:22

achieve a revocation of the General Order. The Post Chaplain admonished us with the following scripture: "Woe unto them that are mighty to drink wine, and men of strength to mingle strong drink." I felt his sermon most timely.

Dear Diary,

Wagon loads of medicine, bedding, and sick soldiers have been rolling into Fort D. A. Russell since last month when Fort Fetterman and Fort Sanders were ordered abandoned. The news of the closures swept through the army grape vine leaving everyone fearful for the future of their own station. Richard feels that the lessening of Indian activity has caused the cutback. He insists that this Post was not established for protection against Indians and therefore should not be effected.

I would hate to leave this place that has been home to me. The Post now resembles a prim little village and I have even grown accustomed to the odors which stifled me when I first arrived. "That atmosphere could best be described as the melded odors of stables, sage brush, dust, gun oil, dressed leather and horse-impregnated uniforms." Even the wide variety of mongrels that roam freely, devastating the grounds, now serve to amuse me. "When the assembled trumpeters sound off at revelry, guardmount, and retreat, they are accompanied by the keening howls of all the dogs on the Post who gather in groups as close to their source of misery as they can get, and cut loose . . . When the trumpeters cease, so do the dogs, and the sudden peace is equally startling." I am so acclimated to this unrefined way of life, I doubt that I could ever live happily any place else.

Richard was most displeased with my purchase of two loaves of bread from the Post Bakery. It is dark in color and dry, "but cannot be said to be unwholesome. It is as good as can be made from the Utah flour furnished . . ." The Enlisted men at the bakery informed me that the flour used is the standard enlisted men's ration flour and is not the quality sold to the officers from the subsistence store house. The rough quality of the bread reminds me of the flour used years ago, milled in the west, called *Rough and Ready*. Richard suggests that I go back to making my own bread!

The officers' wives were all invited to Headquarters to inspect the newly installed telephone instrument. It astonished me to think that one can speak to another person three miles distant. We examined the instrument warily. Standing and talking in whispers, the bell rang, frightening us all. Such changing times we live in! I wonder if the telephone is strictly for the military or if it will be within the bounds of the woman's world.

Medical History of the Post, Microfilm H-62, Wyoming State Archives, Vol. III, May 1882, p. 23

Ibid., April 1882, p. 22

The Troopers, S. E. Whitman, Hasting House Publishers, New York, 1962, pp. 140, 150, 24

Tribune Eagle, Cheyenne, Wyoming, June 14-15, 1967, Section C, p. 6, Col. 2

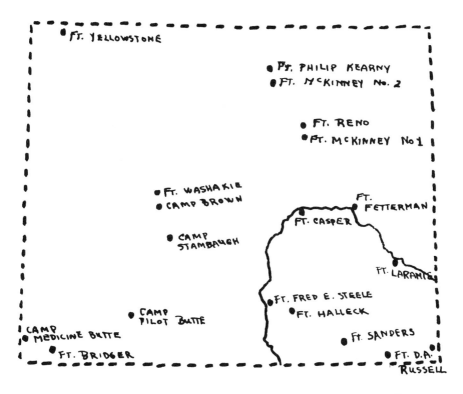

ARMY POSTS OF THE NORTHERN PLAINS

May 1883

Dear Diary,

We have just returned from a most exciting evening ride into Cheyenne. The Inter Ocean Hotel had a gala open-house to celebrate their new electric lights. Even the streets that guided us to the hotel were lined with these fascinating new inventions. We have watched the wiring being installed in several businesses and a few homes during the last year. The lights at the Inter Ocean Hotel were demonstrated to us proudly by the owner. "All day long in the electric plant, storage batteries are charged and when dusk begins to fall these batteries are delivered by wagon to the various homes and business houses wired for electricity. The next morning the batteries are called for and taken back to the plant to be recharged." The owner says that eventually permanent batteries will be installed and in the meantime, extra batteries for parties and special events are furnished. Every corner of the hotel room was ablaze as if the sun was shining. The lights added warmth to our merriment. I look forward to the day when my home at Fort D. A. Russell can be lighted in such an elegant manner.

The changes in the social life of Cheyenne are quite evident. With cattlemen's money, Carey Avenue is now called "Millionaires Row." New church buildings have sprung up to replace temporary frame structures. Social gatherings center in these newly constructed mansions and churches. Many officers of the Fort have joined congregations in town and are invited to the homes of the wealthy for lavish, formal parties and masquerade balls. With all of this money being spent on social affairs and buildings, it is a shame that Cheyenne still has filthy streets "which alternate between dusty and muddy."

An abundance of newly organized clubs have formed to serve a wide variety of interests. The Cheyenne and Fort Russell Gun Clubs compete in matches using live and clay pigeons. Roller skating and cycling clubs are popular among adults as well as children. Territorial baseball and football teams meet Sunday afternoons. I suppose the monotony of the past decade has led men to seek out new friends and common interests. Since my first arrival, I feel that the interaction between people in Cheyenne and the Fort has increased. I think the economic prosperity of the Territory and the lessening of Indian strife has brought people out and together. Whatever the reason, it has enriched our lives.

The Magic City of the Plains, 1867-1967, Wyoming Centennial Historical Committee, July 1967, p. 74
History of Wyoming, T. A. Larson, University of Nebraska Press, 1965, pp. 207, 210

August 1884

Dear Diary,

What wonderful news we received today. Fort D. A. Russell has been made a permanent military post. We are all breathing easier now that we know we shall not be faced with fort abandonment as so many have been in the past. The announcement by the Post Commander has turned loose a most unprecedented revelry and I can hear, even from inside the house, the most unusual outbursts of enthusiasm. I might suggest that it would not be unlikely that the Guard House will be overflowing in the morning.

Lieutenant James Regan of the 9th Infantry informed Richard that a great many requests for reports on the conditions of the buildings here are arriving from different officials in the Department of the Platte. There are also requests for detailed estimates for everything necessary upon which to form plans for a complete post. I was spellbound as he described hoped-for new buildings and particularly new officers' quarters. The quarters were described as two story brick edifices too grand to believe. When Captain J. H. Lord from Camp Carlin stated that as much as $100,000 was granted for the rebuilding of Fort Russell, I felt inwardly that Richard and I would be fortunate to be here to watch the changes take place. It appeared, as the conversation continued, that very little would go untouched at the Fort and even our frame quarters might be the recipient of much needed repair. I could not help but let my mind wander and I suspect that I was planning not for a military establishment, but rather for a gracious abode on the plains. Nothing was beyond the bounds of my imagination and I savored every thought; such pleasant thoughts after so many years of anguish over Indian strife.

Captain Lord permitted the men to look at several proposed plans, at which time I suggested that my curiousity insisted upon having a look also. The plans were beautiful and included Non-Commissioned Officers' Quarters, Captains' Quarters, Company Barracks, Field Officers' Quarters, Warehouses, an Ice House, a Magazine, an Oil House, and even a Bakery. Such elegant buildings and all of brick, reminded me of those pleasant Eastern posts, so sheltered and so civilized.

I suppose that we will spend much time in waiting for the Army to approve or disapprove different plans. Thank goodness they have decided that this Post has a strategic location on the railroad and should be permanent. Even if none of the changes take place, the moments of unloosed gaity and imagination have sparked the lives of us all.

Report of the Quartermaster General, 30 June 1886, Government Printing Office, Washington, p. 96

"Russel L. Tracy Memoirs," Mark Chapman Collection, Wyoming State Archives, pp. 2-3

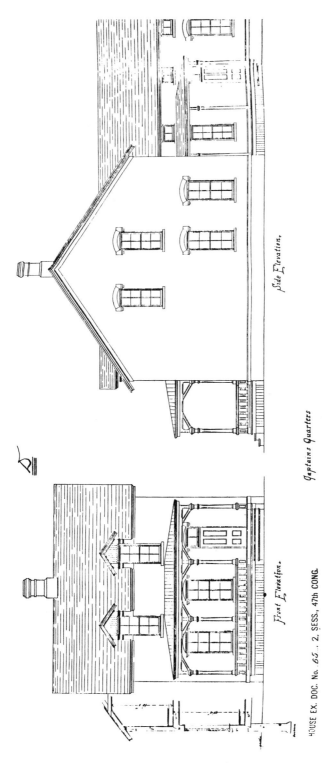

Captains Quarters

Side Elevation.

Front Elevation.

HOUSE EX. DOC. No. 65—2. SESS., 47th CONG.

Proposed plan of Captains' Quarters built in 1885 and 1888. *Executive Documents of the House of Representatives*, 1883, Serial 2108.

85

Dear Diary,

The newspaper reported an incident involving Chinese miners in Rock Springs that upset me. On the night of September 2nd, some drunk white men, angered by the labor dispute in the mines, killed twenty-eight Chinese and wounded fifteen others. They chased several hundred out of their homes and destroyed thousands of dollars worth of property.

It seems that after the railroad was completed, a large Chinese community grew up in Rock Springs. The coal mines became their means of support. Their labor was cheap and everyone felt they were honest workers who performed their jobs well. For ten years they lived peacefully until the discovery of gold in the Black Hills. All types of men abandoned their jobs and came to find their fortune in the Territory. I feel that these newcomers are the culprits in the dispute. When they were unsuccessful in the gold fields, they turned to honest labor. The mine owners would not hire them for the pay that they demanded. I assume they felt if they could scare the Chinese away, the mine owners would have no choice but to hire them. The poor people ran from their homes for fear of their lives. My Army experience has taught me to fear for my life at times, and no one should be subject to such abuse as this.

I received a letter from William and it appears that he is settled nicely in his new surroundings. He feels that he is academically ready for his assigned course of study, but socially out of his element. He has been the brunt of practical jokes by his classmates. He appears to accept it in the spirit of sport. The decision to send him to the military preparatory school in Massachusetts was not easy. Richard felt strongly that it was time for him to loose the apron ties. I guess I agree in principle, but there are times when I miss him desperately. It is hard to realize that he is already into his fifteenth year.

Richard has asked for leave again. Since our short wedding journey in December of 1878, he has not been granted a leave of absence. If by some chance the Army should see fit to honor his request, we have been invited to visit old friends now stationed in Washington, D. C. I am now making preparations in the hope that the Army will not disappoint us once more. With things quiet now, Richard feels the time is right.

History of Wyoming, T. A. Larson, University of Nebraska Press, 1965, p. 141

Dear Diary,

Leave time was granted and we said a quick good-by to our friends at Fort D. A. Russell, and boarded the train for Washington. We stayed with friends I had met a long time ago, the Harmong's. He is now a Commodore on duty at the Navy Department and he and Richard had much to talk about.

The whole city of Washington excited me. It had broad streets, large parks, and the most interesting people. Mrs. Harmong took me to the home of Mrs. William Whitney, wife of the Secretary of the Navy, for an afternoon. I found her to be a most charming hostess, with the "facility of making each one (guest) feel that he or she was the desired guest." At another social engagement, we had dinner at the home of an Army friend of Richard's. While at dinner, two officers' cards were brought to me and I was surprised at the formality, "as I had never seen a visiting card during my years I had lived on the frontier."

The high-light of the whole trip was the reception given at the White House by President and Mrs. Cleveland. "I shall never forget the scene as they came down the stairs and passed through the hall, lined on either side with diplomats from all countries in full court-dress, Army and Navy officers in full dress uniform, judges of the Supreme Court, ladies in gorgeous gowns covered with jewels, Senators, Members of Congress, and civilians. As Mrs. Cleveland passed me on the arm of the President to go into the Blue Room, I was thrilled with emotion; she was so young and fair and wore her honors so easily and gracefully that it was no wonder she won all hearts all over our land, regardless of party." With some cakes and drinks, and toasts to the President, the evening ended all too quickly for me.

While Richard continued his business, I was given a few days on my own, and went to visit some Army people. Their life was so different from mine, that I found little in common with them. The women were not close as a group; I guess the frontier made my Army Sisters depend upon each other. Life here was not simple; even dinner invitations had to be sent out a week in advance. Washington society was demanding on the time of all who participated. The pace of life was fast. There seemed to be little time to enjoy all the reading matter which lured me to every book shop and magazine and newspaper stand.

Since Richard and I had the trip in front of us, we decided to use the time and share some of our experiences. He found the men kind and understanding, but formal in manner. The one thing that he had enjoyed especially was a "salon" he visited in the apartment of a Mrs.

Reminiscences of a Soldier's Wife, Ellen McGowan Biddle, J. B. Lippincott Co., 1907, pp. 217, 224, 216, and 218

Loring of Boston. He met many men of distinction from government officials to artists, and the "tone of her house was decidedly intellectual and enjoyable."

Of course, there are so many benefits to living in a big city, but I must admit, when it was time to return to Wyoming, I thought to myself 'there is no place like home.'

President and Mrs. Grover Cleveland. Mrs. Cleveland's photo courtesy of Wyoming State Archives. President Cleveland's photo taken from *A Man Four Square*, Denis Tilden Lynch, New York, 1932

Dear Diary,

This will be a winter to be remembered for many years to come. The weather has been so impossible, that it goes beyond my imagination how to describe or digest what has happened to the Fort, the town, and the Territory. A combination of extremely heavy snow falls, blizzards, and spring rains that led to hurricanes, has left us all in a state of shock. Buildings, people, and animals have had a rough time surviving the hollicust. The paper reported that one-third of the total northern range cattle have died. "Poor starving cattle which were driven into the city from the surrounding country, by the storms and cold, looked in vain for something to eat. They seemed to have a sort of instinctive idea, that if they could get where man was their wants would be supplied . . ." They huddled close to buildings to get out of the high winds and heavy snows. Their very presence in town and at Fort D. A. Russell, has created many problems. They have destroyed small out buildings on the Post, tramped where gardens once grew, and have created a sanitation problem for all of us.

I feel so sorry for men like John Hunton, who invested in cattle and over extended themselves. These men have lost everything. Richard says that the way the situation stands now, the remaining cattle that lived through this ordeal, will not bring much at the market. They are too thin and scrawny. Everyone in the cattle business is in debt; Cheyenne business people are feeling the squeeze of tight money. Thank goodness we are in the Army and the paymaster comes, no matter what the weather.

In town, the talk is depressing. I overheard one of the shop owners where I buy my produce say that Wyoming is "hell on women and horses and death on cattle." The cattle barons, who built beautiful mansions along Carey Avenue are all effected. No one knows what is going to happen to "Millionaires Row." In the meantime, lots of men have been gathering at the Cheyenne Club. Richard is a member, and tells me a little of the many problems facing the cattle men. Credit having been extended to them, they have all reinvested in their herds. They never bother to keep an accurate head count, so some don't know how many they really lost. The bottom seems to have fallen out

Article written by Mr. Hayford, editor of Laramie paper, 1881, as it appeared in *History of Wyoming*, T. A. Larson, University of Nebraska Press, 1965, p. 191

Medical History of the Post, microfilm H-62, Wyoming State Archives, March 1887

John Hunton Diaries, Volume 6, 1885-1889, The Arthur H. Clark Co., Glendale, California, 1970

History of Wyoming, T. A. Larson, University of Nebraska Press, 1965, pp. 192, 195, 197

of the territorial economy, and talk about statehood is now being put off until the present condition can be assessed.

Those who have brick quarters at the Fort came through this period much better than the rest of us. Although building construction is at a standstill, Richard says that our turn to get new quarters will come soon. I am very much looking forward to the change.

August 1888

Dear Diary,

The comings and goings of Army families continue to keep our social life busy. One of the more interesting teas was held yesterday afternoon, with all of the officers' wives in attendance. It turned into a time to reminisce of days past with the Army. Old stories attributed to famous men were told. The remark made by General Sheridan about Texas set us all laughing, especially those who had spent time there. It went like this: "If I owned hell and Texas, I'd live in hell and rent out Texas." Another went "Texas and Arizona would equal any state in the Union if they only had plenty of water and good society—which is all that hell lacks."

Discussing Texas brought memories to one woman, of time spent there, with the Negro cavalry. Her husband had served as one of their officers. She said that they were a delightful group of men and that her husband confessed "that on long and monotonous field service and when troubled with a depression of spirits, they (officers) have only to go about the campfires of the Negro soldier in order to be amused and cheered by their clever absurdities . . ." She said that although they might have been hungry and tired, they did not fight among themselves. She had been with them in Texas and saw them fight gallantly in the Victorio War of 1879-1880. At that time, "both Generals Ord and Pope acknowledged, the black soldiers who pursued Victorio had endured some of the most punishing ordeals in the history of the Indian Wars." Most were illiterate, which left all the paper work to their white officers, but they performed well on campaigns and listened and took orders well.

It is obvious that the Army has offered to the Negro man, a real career. The conversation got too serious when we started to discuss racially mixing the guards. One woman felt it "was outrageous to put white and black in the same little guard room, and colored sergeants over white corporals and privates." Another lady came to the defense of the 'buffalo soldiers' and soon a confrontation ensued. It was soon settled, but it is clear that strong feelings still remain from the Civil War, and racial prejudice is a part of the Army system.

The tea soon ended and good-bys were said, but the strained feeling among the ladies was still evident.

The Troopers, S. E. Whitman, Hasting House Publishers, New York, 1962, p. 17

Frontier Regulars, Robert Utley, Macmillan Co., New York, 1973, pp. 27-28, 374

The Buffalo Soldiers, William H. Leckie, University of Oklahoma, Norman, 1967, Chap. IV, p. 81

Jerry Spore

Dear Diary,

The end of an era is approaching as regimental co-operative stores have been authorized to replace post traders' stores. The variety of items carried by the new canteens is similar to those previously carried by the trader. The major change appears to be the forced leisure-time separation of officers and enlisted men. Although their drinking always took place in separate rooms, now they will have clubs in individual buildings. Richard explained to me that the profits of these canteens go to the troop mess funds "to purchase additions to relieve the monotony of regulation issue chow." I hope this proves to be a solution to the overall health problems of the enlisted men.

Although the Post trader has always had a friendly, congenial atmosphere, there is no question that some of his offerings contributed to the problems of the troops. President Hayes banned the sale of lightening whiskey by the traders in 1881. This ban led to the great surge of "hog ranches" outside of most every post, providing "whiskey of scandalous content, card tables, and often feminine pleasures." I trust that the new canteen system may bring a return and satisfaction of recreational needs at the Post itself.

In his efforts to accommodate the needs of his clientele, the post trader provided special services. ". . . two or three wheelbarrows were always kept beside the bar so that customers, unable to navigate, could more easily be returned to barracks by their friends." He also acted as a banker, cashing checks and making loans. For recreation he provided billiard tables, reading rooms with papers and magazines, and general merchandise for army as well as civilian travelers. "The post trader sold tinned delicacies, and at times, fresh foods at prices that customers eagerly paid, even though exorbitant."

For years post traders were appointed with the approval of Washington. It was considered a political reward. It certainly was lucrative to the man who was designated to the position. This system was an improvement, however, over its predecessor, the post sutler, who was under the province of the whims of the Post Commander.

It appears that the coming of the canteen marks the end of the era of spoils. The army is becoming more self-sufficient and private entrepreneurs will no longer be necessary to meet the needs of the troops. Change comes very slowly in the army, but it comes.

The Troopers, S. E. Whitman, Hastings House Publishers, New York, 1962, pp. 143, 129, 20

Frontier Regulars, Robert M. Utley, Macmillan Co., New York, 1973, pp. 89, 90

Spurs to Glory, James M. Merrill, Rand McNally Co., 1966, p. 85

Coins courtesy of Thomas Mason and Charles Sorenson. *Photo by Eric Johnson.*

Dear Diary,

Richard reminds me regularly that the area of military discipline is an area in which I have no recourse but to remain silent. I listen to the mens' discussions and cannot help but laugh to myself over certain incidents, although I do abide by my husband's wishes in the matter.

The Post Surgeon at Fort D. A. Russell described a letter from Dr. O'Reilly in which charges were brought against Private Albert Betz of Company G, 7th Infantry. Private Betz was a patient in the hospital at Fort Logan, Colorado, suffering from a fistula contracted in the line of duty. Being placed on the "convalescent list" from time to time, he was ordered to assist in weeding the hospital grounds by the Hospital Steward. Hospital Steward Alfred Baur was then assaulted by Betz who picked up a stone and attempted to throw it at him. Betz also used obscene and abusive language. Private Adam Stauch attempted to prevent the stone from leaving his hands at which time Betz "feloniously assaulted Stauch by biting him upon the thumb, with the intent to do serious bodily harm." He also refused to take a certain medicine, thereby delaying and endangering his cure. Betz was at once placed in the guard house. A trial was held at which time he was sentenced to a general court martial.

Betz determined to appeal to the Secretary of War for relief and explained that he was "required to perform much laborious work such as scrubbing, sweeping, and cook's police, all of which gave him more or less pain and perhaps delayed his cure." He stated that when the Hospital Steward ordered him to pull weeds in the grounds around the hospital, "as this stooping over and straining he knew would give him excessive pain, he lost his temper and refused to obey the order." His appeal was to no avail.

I wonder if the man was really in pain or if he was using the disease to excuse himself from work. According to the conversation of the men, his behavior was certainly improper regardless of the cause. Men in the hospital, who are not bed-ridden, have always been required to do labors in and around the building. They are usually light and are not dangerous to the health of the men. I think the Army feels that if they are paying a man and he can do work, he should.

Disobeying orders is taken very seriously in the military; a small squabble between men leads into a court martial, while the same incident between two women, would be settled within a few moments.

Charles R. Greenleaf Manuscript Collection, National Library of Medicine, Bethesda, Maryland

Dear Diary,

Wyoming was officially declared a state on the 10th of July. Great celebration sprang from within the hearts of everyone. It seemed like such a long-waited for decision. At last Richard is serving our country without the stigma associated with territorial backwardness. We belong!

The statehood celebration parade assembled at Fort D. A. Russell and proceeded to Cheyenne, with the military men in full dress uniform and the Post band playing enthusiastically. Company K and H of the girl guard gathered also, dressed alike for the occasion. I have never seen such gaiety and jubilation. Speeches rang out from every street corner, songsters filled the air, and among the men, the liquor flowed profusely. I shall never forget that day and how to me it symbolized the passing of an era.

Camp Carlin was abandoned in March and most of the stores were transferred to Fort Robinson, Nebraska. Some of the buildings were sold to Cheyenne residents while others were moved to the Post. "Thirty handsome cottonwoods which formerly stood at Camp Carlin have been taken up and replanted at the Fort. The trees are very large, being over fifteen years old."

Sewer and water systems have been completed during the year; the sewerage being connected with that of the town of Cheyenne. I suspect that these are the most important improvements ever made at the Fort.

News of more Indian troubles has arrived from Wounded Knee, South Dakota. Perhaps I was too quick to assume the passing of an era. Indian leaders started talking of an Indian Messiah who would come in and lead them to their final victory against the white man. The Sioux jumped the reservation and about 1,800 of them gathered in the Bad Lands and worked themselves into a high pitch with dancing, vapor baths, and 'ghost dancing' along with oratory. The government sent men to pick up Sitting Bull so that he would provide no leadership for this group. In explaining his intention to the Indians, a Lieutenant was killed and in turn, two Indian police sergeants killed Sitting Bull. Most of the Indians retreated to Wounded Knee Creek where they joined another group led by Big Foot. Forsyth was sent to parley to get the Indians to return to their reservations. Troopers searched the tepees and

The History of Wyoming, C. G. Coutant, Chaplin, Spafford and Mathison, Laramie, 1899, Vol. I, p. 597

The Annals of Wyoming, "History of Fort Francis E. Warren," Jane Kendall, No. 1, January 1946, Col. 1, p. 26

Military Customs and Traditions, Major Mark M. Boatner III, David McKay Co., New York, 1956, p. 196

found fifty rifles. One Indian pulled out a hidden gun, and the battle began. The battle enraged for seven hours with the Regulars finally succeeding in subduing the Indians.

Each time I begin to feel secure and comfortable, something happens which brings me back to the realization that life in the region is not thoroughly humanized. Although we are now a state, when will we ever enjoy the security taken for granted by our Eastern countrymen?

Courtesy Wyoming State Archives

May 1892

Dear Diary,

The events of the last month at Fort D. A. Russell are most strange to tell. It started out with some men leaving on the train to head north to Johnson County. The party was made up of wealthy, educated, and predominantly eastern gentlemen who were cattlemen. They had been challenged by a new group made up of small independent cattlemen, who joined together and formed themselves into the 'Northern Wyoming Farmers and Stockgrowers Association.' The main bone of contention was the unwritten law concerning the ownership of mavericks. The Wyoming Stockgrowers Association, of which these educated men were members, contended that those animals belonged to their herds, while the newly formed group maintained they belonged to no one until a brand had been put on them. The Independents intent to have a round-up has been advertised in the newspapers. So the challenge has been made.

The fifty men of the cattle baron group, last month, cornered two men in a cabin and killed them both; they pinned a note on their bodies "cattle thieves, beware." The papers have christened the affair the Johnson County War. The men were met with lynch talk and only through the efforts of the President of the United States and the aid of Federal troops, were the fifty saved. They were brought here under guard, but the 'prisoners' only numbered forty-four. They were treated like royalty, being allowed to go into town and some have even left to return to their homes; others have left the state. I have never seen anything like this in my life. It is not the military way, yet everyone stands around doing nothing. When they left here, they were taken to the penitentiary in Laramie, where the paper reported they were greeted with a "guard of honor, which included Wyoming's Adjutant General and the Acting Secretary of State."

Public opinion seems to depend on who you talk to. The cattlemen here are for the invaders, while the general public seems to be against them. Their behavior and treatment is the subject of much discussion among the women here at the Post.

Another topic of discussion is Mrs. Schalk and her son, George, who live on the southern edge of the reservation. For six years she has made daily rounds of the Post delivering milk to the garrison. She has infuriated every Commanding Officer by appropriating items from the walls of the stables, and anything else that is not nailed down. Her

American Heritage, "The Johnson County War," Helena Huntington Smith, April 1961, Vol. XII, No. 3, pp. 50-53 and 74-77
Letters Received Quartermaster General, 22 September 1892, Record Group 92, National Archives, Letter No. 165

wagon can be seen daily entering the Post with milk cans and leaving with a variety of Quartermaster stores. The women say "both the Mother and son are little, if any more than half-witted. The son has the cunning of the idiot and he is capable of any crime. I have never seen him sober enough to either talk or understand intelligently." Everyone considers them a nuisance and even civil authorities have arrested her from time to time. Her latest caper was in closing the south gate leading out of the reservation. She denied the military the right to travel over the road although it is a public highway. I assume she wants to extract payment from the government for use of what she considers her land. The children follow the wagon imitating George's queer antics and although I do not approve, I find myself also amused by the whole situation.

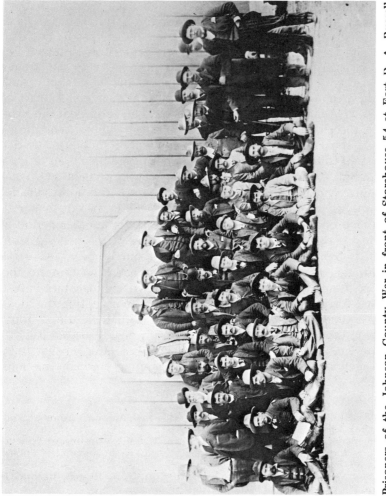

Prisoners of the Johnson County War in front of Storehouse 54 at Fort D. A. Russell.
Courtesy of Wyoming State Archives.

October 1892

Dear Diary,

Since our return from the East and with William living there, Richard and I now take a weekly Eastern paper. This week it brought us the happy news that Doctor Charles Alden, one of my first friends at Fort D. A. Russell and the first Post Surgeon, has just been appointed Dean of the new Army Medical School. Richard never had the pleasure of meeting this gentleman and so I told him of his courtesies during my confinement and after the birth of William. I remember Aunt Elizabeth telling me that he and General Stevenson, the first Post Commander, drew up the plans for the Post, its form taking that of a triangle.

My own personal feeling is that the man is a genious. I know that he designed the plans for St. Mark's Church, along with some help from Reverend Cook and the rest of the building committee. He also put "The Last Supper upon one of the chancel window panes and succeeded very well." He built things for the hospital, such as shelves, and still had plenty of time to read. I remember that he could speak French and German, and one of our little games was to throw French phrases at each other during social gatherings, much to the annoyance of the other guests. He had a world of knowledge about the surrounding area, both its history and its natural wonders. As part of his duties as Post Surgeon, he was obliged to keep records of the weather, describe the flora and fauna, report on the buildings, sanitation, and health of the Post, and take care of seemingly a million other details. He was said to be a good surgeon too. I have fond memories of the man and wish him well on his way toward the Surgeon General's Office.

Things here at the Post are not going well. The houses are falling into disrepair and the Quartermaster tells us he has no materials to make the proper restoration. It seems we are in another period when the Army is out of face with Congress. One of the first signs of this 'disease' is the crumbling and decaying of our homes. Well, we have lived through this before and we shall do it again—we have no choice!

Two Remington Standard No. 3 typewriting machines have been requested for this Post. The Army seems to be accepting the idea that not only time but legibility is improved with their use. I hope the requisition is not at an inopportune time, although I suspect it is.

The Commanding Officer of the Post has directed that trains of the Cheyenne and Northern Railway running through the military

"Personal Report," Record Group 94, National Archives, Compartment 14, Row 22, Box 1

Diary and Letters of the Reverend Joseph W. Cook, Missionary of Cheyenne, arranged by the Rt. Rev. N. S. Thomas, S.T.D., Laramie Republican Publishers, 1919, pp. 56, 60, 77

Letters Sent-Quartermaster Department, Fort D. A. Russell, Record Group 393, National Archives, 1892 Series, Letters No. 34 and 126.

reservation, shall not exceed the rate of six miles an hour. Perhaps trains are fast and convenient, but I still prefer the pleasures of horse drawn conveyances.

Charles Alden, Post Surgeon at Fort D. A. Russell—1867-1871. *Copy provided by Maj. Gen. James A. Wier, National Archives photo.*

Dear Diary,

Poor Molly Frohwein has just laid her husband to rest. The Post cemetery now holds three from the same family, as two of their children preceded him in death.

He was a hospital steward here, and was sent off to the Spanish American War just a few months ago. His duties in the war were to care for the yellow fever victims and he succumbed to the disease himself. "His body was sent back by President McKinley and on the casket it said 'not to be opened, contagious disease'."

The first time I met him in the Post hospital, it was obvious that he was a real gentleman. I later found out that he was an officer in the German army before coming to America. He was a practicing physician there, but was unwilling to accept the unknown duties of a Post Surgeon in the army. He therefore became a hospital steward whose duties included house calls to sick patients. On one of these calls he met Molly Downey. He cared for her and they were married soon thereafter. They took up residence on the second floor of the hospital in one of the two apartments, the other being used by Hospital Steward Unger.

Emil was a talented man who indulged himself in the playing of the violin, singing "Molly Darling" to his wife, and writing beautiful poetry. He was called upon by his associates to play the role of Cyrano de Bergerac, writing poetry that would woo their ladies.

Unlike most widows who are forced to leave the Post soon after their loss, Molly will take up residence with her father who is the sanitary engineer and lives at the Pump House by Crow Creek. Her young son and daughter will accompany her. I feel they may be somewhat restricted in space as the pump house has only two bedrooms. It is a blessing that they will have family close by for moral and financial support.

Strange occurrences are being noticed at Fort D. A. Russell. All of the quarters are flanked by the family cows which have recently been dehorned. The mystery was solved when we noticed in town, Indians standing on the corner selling polished bone projections, unmistakeably the missing horns. It appears their leisurely naps on the wood piles at the Post had alterior motives. The cows look ridiculous and somewhat remind me of a lady in church without her bonnet!

Richard spends his days helping to issue the necessary accouterments for the war to the many raw troops. He amuses me daily with stories of the new recruits' lack of basic knowledge as to which end of the horse to saddle. He wonders if the army will ever have the quality of trooper that took part in the Indian Wars.

Oral History—Mrs. Edna Mawhinney, 23 January 1973, F. E. Warren A.F.B. Museum.

Dr. and Mrs. Emil Frohwein. *Courtesy of Mrs. Edna Mawhinney.*

Dear Diary,

I do not understand why it always takes a war to bring the people to their senses. Over the years the Army has coped with periods of bitter struggle to stay in existence. Now sentiment seems to favor the need of a standard army. I remember in 1893 with the closing of the frontier, the question arising as to the need and purpose of having an army in the West. Appropriations were very low and military reservations "fell into disrepair, and in the case of Fort D. A. Russell, almost dilapidation." Now with the general acceptance of a need for the Army, appropriations are again being adopted and another period of change and construction is taking place.

In May Senator Warren received a message that additional funds have been designated for Fort D. A. Russell. New brick quarters have been constructed during this year including some new duplexes for officers and a bachelor officers quarters. The new money will mean "that all the old frame buildings at the Post which have been used for Officers' quarters will be replaced with good, substantial brick and stone houses." Everyone is greatly relieved as all occupants of frame quarters agree that these quarters have outlived their usefulness. Not only are they uncomfortable, but unsatisfactory feelings exist when your neighbors live adjacent in large, brick houses.

Many changes have taken place in our familiar surroundings. The Wyoming National Guard has been issued a license to use the Camp Carlin portion of the reservation as a pasturage. Although Camp Carlin was dismantled in 1890, I remember fondly, so many happy occasions there prior to that time. Part of the military maneuver area at Pole Mountain has been set aside as a forest reserve.

From the talk among the officers here, part of the reason for the expansion of the Army, is that we did not fair well during the war. Congress feels that this is in part due to the lack of funds and training for this new kind of war; one fought on foreign soil. It is obvious to the ladies here at the Post, that with the end of this conflict, America has taken a new leadership position in the affairs of the world. We all wonder how this will effect our future lives.

Denver Times, 24 May 1900, p. 9, Col. 5, Microfilm No. 53, Western History Division, Denver Public Library

United States Military Reservations, National Cemeteries and Military Parks, Government Printing Office, Washington, D. C., 1910, pp. 451-453

Double Set Officers' Quarters constructed in 1900. *Fort D. A. Russell*, Book 1, *courtesy F.E. Warren A.F.B. Museum.*

Dear Diary,

I feel I have accomplished a singular honor in my lifetime, having met two Presidents of the United States. The first was on my trip to Washington, D. C. in the winter of 1885 when I was honored to attend a reception at the White House with President and Mrs. Cleveland. Now this spring, President Teddy Roosevelt came to Fort D. A. Russell at which time I prepared tea for him. Having spent most of my life residing in the unpopulated west, it is curious that I should be permitted to savor such memories of these dignified men of distinction.

President Roosevelt made a trip through the Southwest returning eastward on the Union Pacific Railroad. He consented to deliver the Memorial Day address in Cheyenne. Plans were made that he should leave the train in Laramie and ride horseback from there, with an escort of prominent citizens, to Cheyenne. "He approved the idea with great enthusiasm" being a man who loved the strenuous life. The route was across the Continental Divide through forests and mountain streams. We all watched with great interest the newspapers which described the progress of the ride, word being relayed through the ranch telephone lines. Dinner was taken at the Van Tassell Ranch and then the ride proceeded to a point three miles from Fort Russell where Governor Fennimore Chatterton greeted the President. They than "rode into Fort Russell where Major Foster, the Commandant, and the ladies gave them tea and cakes." The President and the Governor "reviewed the troops by riding past the line which wheeled into line behind them for the three-mile march to the speaker's platform in Cheyenne."

I had expected to find the President worn and fatigued after such a ride. "I recall . . . my deep amazement when I saw Col. Roosevelt arrive, sitting his horse in perfect form, alight without effort, shake the hands of the old veterans warmly." "The West was written in every line of his frame, and clothes and bearing: he might have been a ranchman leading a round-up gang for all the chance observer knew—yet there was something about him, an indescribable air of subdued authority, that marked him a greater leader of men."

Richard and I laughed later how of all the arrivals at the Fort, President Roosevelt seemed the freshest, despite his years away from rugged experiences. His endurance is remarkable. I can't help but feel that the United States has a man of great quality in President Roosevelt.

Yesterday's Wyoming, An Autobiography by Fennimore Chatterton, Powder River Publishers and Booksellers, 1957, pp. 28-29, 70-71
Roosevelt in the Bunk House and Other Sketches, William Chapin Deming, The Laramie Printing Company, Laramie, pp. 20-24

President Roosevelt inspecting the troops. *Courtesy of F.E. Warren.*

Dear Diary,

The time has come to end my army diary. Richard is now retiring and our military days are over. My life with the army has had its joy and its sorrow. It has not been an easy life, but it has not been without pleasure.

I recall my arrival at Fort D. A. Russell as a young woman. I was not at ease with the desolate plains and windswept garrison. My whole view changed when I met Charles, as the garrison then became my neighborhood and the rough frame quarters became my home. The birth of William completed our cherished family. Although we were not permitted much time together, the love shared gave me strength for the future. I did not realize that a chance meeting would bring me back into the army circle once more. I am glad that it did.

I have witnessed the Territory become an integral part of the States. Even the surrounding countryside is now settled and ranches break the monotony of the prairie. "Wire fences have long since superceded the fences of an earlier date that were built 'horse high, bull strong, and pig tight'." Ranch homes are connected by telephone with each other and distant places.

Army life has evolved as civilization has progressed. Forts are no longer outposts of inconvenience. The officer's wife now finds herself in comfortable quarters surrounded by helping hands, mechanical wonders, and the luxury of free time. The young women embarking as military wives today, do not comprehend what we veterans have been through. Their complaints sound shallow.

As I look around the Fort I see painted buildings, planted trees, and luscious vegetation, which bring me great pleasure. It is curious to think that children will be playing happily on this historic ground, unaware of its significant past.

I have spent my life struggling from bugs to blizzards, but I would not have changed it. My heart has been filled with joy from loved-ones and the army spirit of sharing a new adventure. What more could life have offered, than the unexpected wonder which has filled each of my days.

My Army Life, Frances C. Carrington, J. B. Lippincott Co., Philadelphia, 1910, p. 235

LIKE A HICK'RY COG
IN THE OLD MILL WHEEL,
SHE DID HER PART
AS HER TURN CAME 'ROUND.

Apples of Gold